MW01052798

justinguitar.com
Beginner's Songbook

Volume II

Published by
Wise Publications
14-15 Berners Street, London W1T 3LJ, UK.

Exclusive Distributors:
Music Sales Limited
Distribution Centre, Newmarket Road,
Bury St Edmunds, Suffolk IP33 3YB, UK.
Music Sales Corporation
180 Madison Avenue, 24th Floor,
New York NY 10016, USA.
Music Sales Pty Limited
Level 4, Lisgar House,
30-32 Carrington Street
Sydney, NSW 2000 Australia

Order No. AM1011197
ISBN: 978-1-78558-135-9
This book © Copyright 2015 Wise Publications,
a division of Music Sales Limited.

Unauthorised reproduction of any part of this
publication by any means including photocopying
is an infringement of copyright.

Written, compiled and arranged by Justin Sandercoe.
Edited by Toby Knowles.
Cover design by Paul Agar.
Cover photographs by Nick Delaney.
With thanks to Dario Cortese.

Printed in the EU.

justinguitar.com
Beginner's Songbook

Volume II

Wise Publications
part of The Music Sales Group
London / New York / Paris / Sydney / Copenhagen / Berlin / Madrid / Hong Kong / Tokyo

Your Guarantee of Quality
As publishers, we strive to produce every
book to the highest commercial standards.
This book has been carefully designed to
minimise awkward page turns and to make
playing from it a real pleasure.
Particular care has been given to specifying
acid-free, neutral-sized paper made from pulps
which have not been elemental chlorine bleached.
This pulp is from farmed sustainable forests and was
produced with special regard for the environment.
Throughout, the printing and binding have been
planned to ensure a sturdy, attractive publication
which should give years of enjoyment.
If your copy fails to meet our high standards,
please inform us and we will gladly replace it.

www.musicsales.com

www.justinguitar.com

Contents

INTRODUCTION

 Welcome to my Beginner's Songbook, Volume 2!

This book is designed to be used in conjunction with my *Beginner's Course*, which is an online series of almost 100 lessons to get you started in the right way on guitar. The course has been used by many hundreds of thousands of people all over the world, and is probably the most-used guitar method ever! You can use it for free, although supporting the site by buying books like this, DVDs or making a donation is very much appreciated and allows me to keep the site going for those that can't afford to contribute. The course is also available in book and CD form, as the *Justinguitar. com Beginner's Course* (AM1001440R).

If you are stuck on a technique, or don't understand something, then your first port of call should be the *Beginner's Course* at the relevant stage—it is very likely you will find your answer there. If you are still stuck then you should post a question to the justinguitar.com forum (www.justinguitarcommunity.com). I use these questions to continually update and improve the website and my books.

This book, which is my second *Beginner's Songbook*, is aimed squarely at beginning guitarists, but adds a few techniques that are beyond beginner level. Compared to my first *Beginner's Songbook*, the learning curve is a little steeper and may take you into unfamiliar territory. Most of the time these extra techniques are optional, and you can still play the songs using simple chords with simple strumming. Learning songs that can grow with you is really rewarding. When you learn a song with easy chords, you then have a vehicle to add further, more advanced techniques, allowing you to learn new chords or strumming patterns in a very practical way.

If a song seems a little hard for the stage it appears in, it is there for a reason: introducing a particular skill. Bear in mind that ALL the songs in this book should be revisited a few times as you progress. Often there are techniques introduced for a song which are deliberately more advanced than the stage that song appears in; these can be looked at further down the line as you get to the later stages.

I plan to make video lessons for most (possibly all) of the songs in this book, and as I do the song will get its own page on my website with related notes alongside the video. I also post links to the original recording (via YouTube) with special live versions, answers to common questions and sometimes extra tips that I couldn't fit in the book! It will also have its own post on the justinguitar.com forum.

I hope that the range of styles represented across the 100 songs in this book—from Bob Marley and Creedence Clearwater Revival to Amy Winehouse and Ed Sheeran—will mean that there are several songs in each stage that you will really like and when combined with my first *Beginner's Songbook*, you will have over 20 songs to choose from in each stage of the *Beginner's Course*!

Wishing you love, peace and happiness,

Justin Sandercoe

November 2015, London

Here's what you'll see for each song!

Look out throughout the book for references to the relevant lesson in the
Beginner's Course online, shown by lesson code: BC-XXX etc.

The tempo (bpm) of the song

Song title

If you need to use a capo to match the key of the original record, the fret to place the capo at is shown here

These tabs show you which stage of the course the song is appropriate for

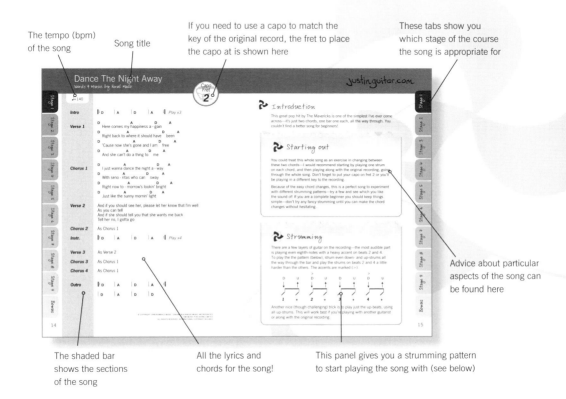

The shaded bar shows the sections of the song

All the lyrics and chords for the song!

This panel gives you a strumming pattern to start playing the song with (see below)

Advice about particular aspects of the song can be found here

Strumming patterns

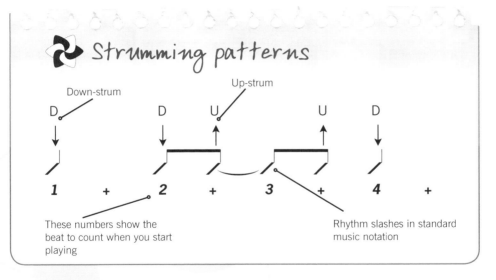

Down-strum

Up-strum

These numbers show the beat to count when you start playing

Rhythm slashes in standard music notation

7

Stage 1

Stage 2

Stage 3

Stage 4

Stage 5

Stage 6

Stage 7

Stage 8

Stage 9

Bonus

STAGE 1 BC-111—BC-119

Introduction

Welcome to Stage 1! At this stage you only learn three chords, and will only be playing simple strumming patterns. Some songs have been simplified rhythmically, so when you play these songs they might not sound *exactly* like the recording—but they will be recognizable as the original song, and as your skills improve the songs will sound better, and more authentic. So, remember to revisit these songs as you progress with the course.

The thing to aim for in Stage 1 is being able to keep your strumming even, when playing at speed, without leaving gaps between the chord changes. At first this might seem impossible—but this is the goal. If you keep working on your 'One-Minute Changes' (see opposite) and picking your chords one note at a time you will soon be able to change between chords quickly and clearly. Don't expect it to come too soon. It WILL take practice—but you WILL get there!

Many of the songs suggest using a capo, but you don't have to use one. A capo will help you play along with the original recording (at the correct pitch), and I recommend that you give this a go once you can play through a song confidently. If you're really keen on using a capo from the start then there is a lesson on my website in Stage 6 (BC-163), but I recommend starting out by just playing the chords in open position, working on your chord changes and keeping your strumming even, bringing in the capo when you are confident with your rhythm playing and want to start working along with the original recorded versions.

It's really helpful when you're starting out to have each chord written for each bar it is played. This concept goes a bit wrong in complex music, or when a chord only lasts half a bar, and this is probably why many sheet music books don't do this (you can always add them in yourself if that is the case). I did that as a kid and found it makes keeping your place in the song a lot easier! So, count along while you sing the words in your head and write the chord in each time you get back to '1' (the start of the bar).

The music in this book isn't written out using full music notation, but we have used barlines to show where some of the chord changes fall. Whenever you see a chord symbol, it almost always means that you play that chord for a full bar (four strums); where two chords are shown between barlines, it almost always means that you play each chord for two beats (two strums) each. Sometimes you'll see a chord symbol in parentheses (e.g., at the beginning of 'You Never Can Tell'). This is simply to indicate where a new section of lyrics begins during the last chord of the previous section, so that you don't play too many strums on that chord.

Stage 1 Chords

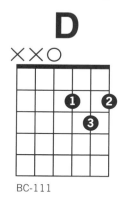

D

BC-111

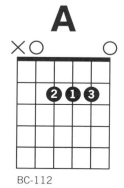

A

BC-112

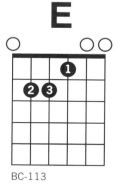

E

BC-113

Stage 1
Stage 2
Stage 3
Stage 4
Stage 5
Stage 6
Stage 7
Stage 8
Stage 9
Bonus

One-Minute Changes BC-115

Once you know how to play your chords, the big challenge is to get your chord changes clear and fast so that you can play a song without stopping between chords. You should be able to do this well before you start trying to play strumming patterns, or your songs will always sound disjointed.

The trick is to focus on changing between two particular chords for one minute. Use a stopwatch, or the countdown feature on your phone, and see how many times you can change between two chords, taking care to hold each one correctly and make each chord ring out clearly.

You will find this will make a huge difference if you stick at it! Do it every day. I see great results with this all the time with my private students and I know you will see a fast improvement too! Keep a record of how many times you make the change each session. You will find that being able to watch your progress will really help keep you motivated.

Strumming four-to-a-bar BC-116

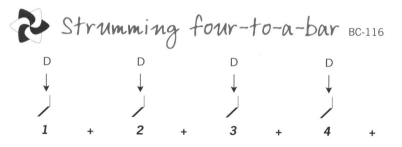

9

Blowin' Smoke

Words & Music by Shane McAnally, Kacey Musgraves & Luke Laird

Stage 1

Stage 2

Stage 3

Stage 4

Stage 5

Stage 6

Stage 7

Stage 8

Stage 9

Bonus

♩=94

Intro | A | D | A | D |

Verse 1
       A
Be - tween the lunch and dinner rush
D   A   D
Kelly caught that outbound bus for Vegas.
                   A
And we're all out here talking trash, making bets,
D
Lips wrapped round our cigarettes,
       A   D
She always thought she was too good to be a waitress.

Pre-Chorus 1
        A   D
Well,   we all say that we'll   quit someday
         A   D   D
When our   ship comes in we'll just   sail away.

Chorus 1
             A   D
But we're just blowin' smoke, hey yeah,
          A   D
We're just blowin' smoke, hey yeah,
     A   D
Out here goin' broke, hey yeah,
          A A
We're just blowin'   smoke.

Verse 2
Well, Janie got divorced again, her ex-husband's in the pen,
For two to five, or five to ten or longer.
And Brenda's traded smokes for cake, still hasn't lost that baby weight,
And that baby's about to graduate from college.

Pre-Chorus 2
I'm just flicking ash into the tray,
Tell them both it'll be okay,

Chorus 2
But I'm just blowin' smoke...

Pre-Chorus 3
We all say that we'll quit someday,
When our nerves ain't shot, and our hands don't shake, yeah,
We all say that we'll quit someday,
         A   D   D
When our   nerves ain't shot, and our   hands don't shake...

Verse 3
Wipe down the bar, take out the trash, light one up and count my cash,
Swear I'm never coming back again.

Chorus 3
As Chorus 2

© COPYRIGHT 2013 WARNER TAMERLANE PUBLISHING CORPORATION/UNIVERSAL MUSIC CAREERS/
LITTLE BLUE EGG/CRAZY WATER MUSIC/351 MUSIC.
KOBALT MUSIC PUBLISHING LIMITED/UNIVERSAL MUSIC PUBLISHING MGB LIMITED/
WARNER/CHAPPELL NORTH AMERICA LIMITED.
ALL RIGHTS RESERVED. INTERNATIONAL COPYRIGHT SECURED.

10

Stage 1

Stage 2

Stage 3

Stage 4

Stage 5

Stage 6

Stage 7

Stage 8

Stage 9

Bonus

Introduction

We'll start with this two-chord hit song, recorded by Kacey Musgraves—it's proof that pop songs don't need to be complicated!

Playing along

This is a great first song to try playing along with the original recording. Make sure you are confident with your two chords (A and D) and with changing between them. Play four down-strums per bar, and when you can change chords without hesitation, you're ready to play along!

The beat or 'pulse' of the song is fairly audible, and played by the kick drum. If you're an absolute beginner you might find it helpful to clap along with the beat, just to become really familiar with it.

Work on getting your chord changes fast enough and the strumming even and consistent, and then enjoy playing! Start by playing four strums per bar—one for each beat (see page 9).

Strumming for real

Once you have that under control, try putting the 'stops' in the right places—this means letting the chord ring out just before, and at the end of the chorus. Listen to the recording to get familiar with the structure and then try to stop and start at the right times. After that you can move on to a slightly harder rhythm—'Old Faithful' (page 19) should serve you well, but if you're a real beginner, try the pattern below.

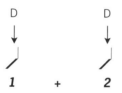

And if you're keen to 'step it up', try playing even eighth-notes and down-strums, accenting (making louder) the strums on beats 2 and 4, which is well beyond stage 1 beginner level but might be fun to try out later!

Bad Moon Rising

Words & Music by John C. Fogerty

Capo Fret
5

♩=180

Intro

| A | E D | A | A |

Verse 1

A |E D |A A
I see a bad moon rising,
A |E D |A A
I see trouble on the way.
A |E D |A A
I see earth - quakes and lightning,
A |E D |A A
I see bad times to - day.

Chorus 1

D D
Don't go around to - night,
A A
Well, it's bound to take your life,
E D A A
There's a bad moon on the rise.

Verse 2

I hear hurricanes a-blowing,
I know the end is coming soon.
I feel rivers overflowing,
I hear the voice of rage and ruin.

Chorus 2

As Chorus 1

Instr.

| A | E D | A | A |

| A | E D | A | A |

| D | D | A | A |

| E | D | A | A |

Verse 3

Hope you got your things together,
Hope you are quite prepared to die.
Looks like we're in for nasty weather,
One eye is taken for an eye.

Chorus 3

Well, don't go around tonight,
Well, it's bound to take your life,
There's a bad moon on the rise.
Don't come around tonight,
Well, it's bound to take your life,
There's a bad moon on the rise.

© COPYRIGHT 1969 JONDORA MUSIC INCORPORATED, USA.
BURLINGTON MUSIC COMPANY LIMITED.
ALL RIGHTS RESERVED. INTERNATIONAL COPYRIGHT SECURED.

Stage 1 Stage 2 Stage 3 Stage 4 Stage 5 Stage 6 Stage 7 Stage 8 Stage 9 Bonus

Introduction

The fabulous Creedence Clearwater Revival serve up a classic song from 1969. We've arranged it for Stage 1 guitarists but it isn't much harder to play 'the real way', so hopefully you'll revisit the song when you know a couple more chords!

Getting started

I always recommend starting with simple down-strums, playing on each beat (four strums per bar), so you can get to know the structure of the song and focus on practising your chord changes. Play this simple pattern along with the original recording, all the way through. Look out for where the E and D chords are in the same bar, meaning that they get two strums each.

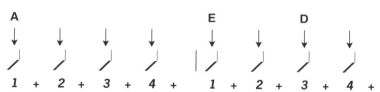

Playing the off beats

Once that's sounding good, add a couple of up-strums as shown in the pattern below, as per the original strumming pattern, but be aware that the last up-strum will often play open strings while you change chords—it may sound a little sloppy, but that's part of what makes this a great record! Just be sure to get your chords in position for beat 1.

D		D		D	U	D	U
↓		↓		↓	↑	↓	↑
1	+	2	+	3	+	4	+

More advanced players can use the original chords (with no capo). Simply play D where I have written A; A where I have written E; and G where I have written D.

Stage 1
Stage 2
Stage 3
Stage 4
Stage 5
Stage 6
Stage 7
Stage 8
Stage 9
Bonus

Dance The Night Away

Words & Music by Raul Malo

Capo Fret
2

Stage 1
Stage 2
Stage 3
Stage 4
Stage 5
Stage 6
Stage 7
Stage 8
Stage 9
Bonus

♩=140

Intro
‖: D | A | D | A :‖ *Play x3*

Verse 1

D　　　　　A　　　　D　　A
Here comes my happiness a - gain
D　　　　　A　　　　　　D　　　A
Right back to where it should have　been
D　　　　　A　　　　　D　　A
'Cause now she's gone and I am　free
D　　　　　A　　　　D　　A
And she can't do a thing to　me

Chorus 1

D　　　　　A　　　　　　D　　A
I just wanna dance the night a - way
D　　　　A　　　　D　　A
With seno - ritas who can　sway
D　　　　　A　　　　　D　　A
Right now to - morrow's lookin' bright
D　　　　A　　　　D　　A
Just like the sunny mornin' light

Verse 2

And if you should see her, please let her know that I'm well
As you can tell
And if she should tell you that she wants me back
Tell her no, I gotta go

Chorus 2　As Chorus 1

Instr.
‖: D | A | D | A :‖ *Play x4*

Verse 3　As Verse 2

Chorus 3　As Chorus 1

Chorus 4　As Chorus 1

Outro
‖: D | A | D | A :‖

| D | A | D | D |

© COPYRIGHT 1998 RUMBALO MUSIC, USA/EMI BLACKWOOD MUSIC INCORPORATED.
EMI MUSIC PUBLISHING LIMITED.
ALL RIGHTS RESERVED. INTERNATIONAL COPYRIGHT SECURED.

Introduction

This great pop hit by The Mavericks is one of the simplest I've ever come across—it's just two chords, one bar one each, all the way through. You couldn't find a better song for beginners!

Starting out

You could treat this whole song as an exercise in changing between these two chords—I would recommend starting by playing one strum on each chord, and then playing along with the original recording, going through the whole song. Don't forget to put your capo on fret 2 or you'll be playing in a different key to the recording.

Because of the easy chord changes, this is a perfect song to experiment with different strumming patterns—try a few and see which you like the sound of! If you are a complete beginner you should keep things simple—don't try any fancy strumming until you can make the chord changes without hesitating.

Strumming

There are a few layers of guitar on the recording—the most audible part is playing even eighth-notes with a heavy accent on beats 2 and 4. To play the pattern (below), strum even down- and up-strums all the way through the bar and play the strums on beats 2 and 4 a little harder than the others. The accents are marked (>).

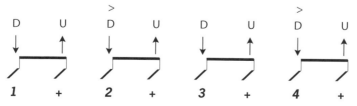

Another nice (though challenging) trick is to play just the up-beats, using all up-strums. This will work best if you're playing with another guitarist or along with the original recording.

Stage 1
Stage 2
Stage 3
Stage 4
Stage 5
Stage 6
Stage 7
Stage 8
Stage 9
Bonus

5 Years Time

Words & Music by Charlie Fink

Stage 1
Stage 2
Stage 3
Stage 4
Stage 5
Stage 6
Stage 7
Stage 8
Stage 9
Bonus

Capo Fret **3**

♩=123

Sequence throughout:

| A   D | E   D |

Intro

Play sequence (free time) *x4*
Play sequence (at speed) *x4*

Verse 1

Oh, well in five years time we could be walking round a zoo,
With the sun shining down over me and you.
And there'll be love in the bodies of the elephants too,
And I'll put my hands over your eyes, but you'll peep through.

Chorus 1

And there'll be sun, sun, sun, all over our bodies.
And sun, sun, sun, all down our necks.
And there'll be sun, sun, sun, all over our faces,
And sun, sun, sun, so what the heck.

Verse 2

'Cause I'll be laughing at all your silly little jokes,
And we'll be laughing about how we used to smoke,
All those stupid little cigarettes and drink stupid wine,
'Cause it's what we needed to have a good time.

Chorus 2

But it was fun, fun, fun, when we were drinking.
It was fun, fun, fun, when we were drunk.
And it was fun, fun, fun, when we were laughing,
It was fun, fun, fun, oh, it was fun.

Link 1

Play sequence *x2*

Verse 3

Oh, well I look at you and say: 'It's the happiest that I've ever been,'
And I'll say: 'I no longer feel I have to be James Dean.'
And she'll say: 'Yeah, well, I feel all pretty happy too,
And I'm always pretty happy when I'm just kicking back with you.'

Chorus 3

And it'll be love, love, love, all through our bodies.
And love, love, love, all through our minds.
And it'll be love, love, love, all over her face.
And love, love, love, all over mine.

Verse 4

Although maybe all these moments are just in my head,
I'll be thinking 'bout them as I'm lying in bed.
And you know that it really, it might not even come true,
But in my mind I'm having a pretty good time with you, oh.

Bridge 1

In five years time I might not know you,
In five years time we might not speak.

© COPYRIGHT 2008 HANGMAN MUSIC LIMITED.
UNIVERSAL MUSIC PUBLISHING LIMITED.
ALL RIGHTS RESERVED. INTERNATIONAL COPYRIGHT SECURED

Stage 1
Stage 2
Stage 3
Stage 4
Stage 5
Stage 6
Stage 7
Stage 8
Stage 9
Bonus

cont.   Oh, in five years time we might not get along,
In five years time you might just prove me wrong.

Link 2   Play sequence *x2*

Chorus 4   Oh, there'll be love, love, love, wherever you go *(x8)*
There'll be love.

 Introduction

Noah And The Whale broke through with this summertime singalong,
released in 2008. Although the tempo is quite fast, it should be easy to
play along with the original recording, especially if you simplify the rhythm.
We're going to be playing the original ukulele part, arranged for guitar, using
a capo on fret 3, so you'll be playing the standard shapes for A, D and E.
Remember that the capo now replaces the nut at the end of the fretboard.

 Strumming

Start by playing just two down-strums per bar, on beats 1 and 3. Play
this simple pattern along with the recording. After this, tap your foot
along with the original recording and try to 'find the beat'—then just
strum down on every strong beat. This means that you'll be strumming
four times per bar.

A		D		E		D	
↓	↓	↓	↓	↓	↓	↓	↓
1	2	3	4	1	2	3	4

To get closer to the recording we need to add some up-strums. The
pattern is very consistent and not too difficult, so take it slowly, get it
right and then gradually speed it up. You might like to use software to
slow the original recording down, so that you can play along and soak
up the groove of the song, before attempting to play at full speed.

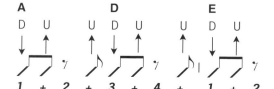

A			D			E			D		
D	U		U	D	U		U	D	U		U	D	U		U
1	+	2	+	3	+	4	+	1	+	2	+	3	+	4	+

Stage 1

Stage 2

Stage 3

Stage 4

Stage 5

Stage 6

Stage 7

Stage 8

Stage 9

Bonus

For What It's Worth

Words & Music by Stephen Stills

♩=98

Intro | E | A | E | A |

Verse 1
E   A
There's something happening here
       E   A
And what it is ain't exactly clear.
       E   A
There's a man with a gun over there,
       E   A
Telling me I've got to be - ware.

Chorus 1
                              | E   D |
I think it's time we stop, children, what's that sound,
A
Everybody look, what's goin' down.

Link 1 | E | A | E | A |

Verse 2
There's battle lines being drawn,
Nobody's right if everybody's wrong.
Young people speaking their minds
Are getting so much resistance from behind.

Chorus 2
It's time we stop, hey, what's that sound,
Everybody look, what's goin' down.

Link 2 | E | A | E | A |

Verse 3
What a field day for the heat,
A thousand people in the street
Singin' songs and carryin' signs,
Mostly say 'Hooray for our side.'

Chorus 3 As Chorus 2

Link 3 | E | A | E | A |

Verse 4
Paranoia strikes deep,
Into your life it will creep.
It starts when you're always afraid,
Step outta line, the man come and take you away.

Chorus 4
We better stop, hey, what's that sound,
Everybody look, what's goin' down,
You better stop, hey, what's that sound,
Everybody look, what's goin' down. *(Repeat Chorus)*

Outro | E | D | A | A | *Fade out*

© COPYRIGHT 1966 COTILLION MUSIC INC./TEN-EAST MUSIC/SPRINGALO TOONES/RICHIE FURAY MUSIC
WARNER/CHAPPELL NORTH AMERICA LIMITED.
ALL RIGHTS RESERVED. INTERNATIONAL COPYRIGHT SECURED.

Introduction

This timeless protest song was written by Stephen Stills, and recorded by the band that he led with Neil Young: Buffalo Springfield. It's a great beginner song—using just three chords—and although you can keep the rhythm really simple, there are some fast-ish changes in the chorus to keep you on your toes!

Strumming

Whatever your standard, you should always start out using very simple strumming. I recommend just four down-strums to the bar (see page 9)—just to get to know the chord changes and the structure of the song. In my songbooks, each chord symbol denotes a whole bar—so you'll play four strums for each chord written, except for the E and D in the chorus which are just two strums each—half a bar. Here you'll see bar lines written on either side of those chords, to show where the bar starts and ends.

Once you've played along with the recording a few times, you should explore some different strumming. In the verses it works great just to strum once at the start of the bar and let the chord ring out. But as the song progresses you might like to add more strums. My go-to strumming pattern for this song is one I call 'Old Faithful'.

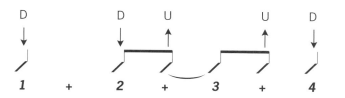

Harmonics

Another nice technique is the harmonics in the lead guitar part. The part is very easy—first play a harmonic at the 12th fret of the thinnest string and let it ring for a bar and then play the harmonic on the 7th fret of the same string and let that ring. They're a fun and easy technique to get to grips with. For a lesson on how to do them and how they work, search on my website for 'natural harmonics'.

Stage 1
Stage 2
Stage 3
Stage 4
Stage 5
Stage 6
Stage 7
Stage 8
Stage 9
Bonus

Me And Charlie

Words & Music by Lee Hazlewood

Stage 1

Stage 2

Stage 3

Stage 4

Stage 5

Stage 6

Stage 7

Stage 8

Stage 9

Bonus

♩=116

Verse 1

```
|A            |D    E   |A      |E      |
 Me and Charlie shot a man this morning,
|A            |D    E   |A      |E      |
 He was such a daring man this morning.
|A            |D    E   |
 His gun was fast and that's a fact,
|A            |D    E   |
 So Charlie shot him in the back,
|A            |D    E   |A      |E      |
 Me and Charlie shot a man this morning.
```

Chorus 1

```
|A    |D      |A   |A       |
 Sing the song some more,
|A    |D      |A  |A  N.C. |
 That's what you're here for.
```

Verse 2

Me and Charlie shot a man this morning,
He was such a greedy man this morning.
Divide his gold he would not do,
So Charlie shot him half in two,
Me and Charlie shot a man this morning.

Chorus 2

As Chorus 1

Verse 3

Me and Charlie we got shot this morning,
Boy, it hurt an awful lot this morning.
Charlie died, what could I do?
So I lay down and I died too,
Me and Charlie we got shot this morning.

Chorus 3

```
|A      |D      |A          |A       |
 Sing the song some more, (there ain't no more)
|A      |D      |A  |A  |A  |A  |
 That's what you're here for.
```

© COPYRIGHT 1965 ATLANTIC MUSIC CORPORATION.
UNIVERSAL MUSIC PUBLISHING LIMITED.
ALL RIGHTS RESERVED. INTERNATIONAL COPYRIGHT SECURED.

20

Justinguitar.com

Stage 1
Stage 2
Stage 3
Stage 4
Stage 5
Stage 6
Stage 7
Stage 8
Stage 9
Bonus

 # Introduction

This isn't exactly a cheerful song, and I'm certainly not condoning shooting people (especially in the back!) but there's something special about this tune—it's simple and fun to play, and Lee Hazelwood is one of my favourite songwriters and producers (he produced some of the great Nancy Sinatra albums).

 # Strumming

Start by keeping the strumming very simple, just playing four down-strums per bar, and looking out for the bars that have just two strums on each chord (where there is a D and an E chord in the same bar). Watch out for the N.C (which means 'No Chord') at the end of the chorus where you will strum once on beat 1 and then remain silent for the rest of the bar.

Once you feel familiar with the song, try this more authentic pattern (below), which uses up-strums as well. Try to keep the feel very loose and relaxed—even if you're struggling with the chord changes, it will sound better if you try to keep everything relaxed.

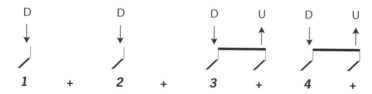

More advanced players might like to pick out the bass notes (the lowest note of each chord) on beats 1 and 3 (you'll learn this in Stage 7 of the *Beginner's Course*), as is the case on the recording, although there are many variations of the pattern throughout the tune. What's more important is getting that fabulous loose and groovy feel, which is best absorbed by playing along (several times) with the original recording.

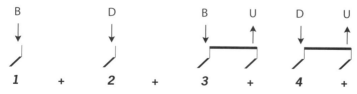

Old Time Rock And Roll

Words & Music by George Jackson & Thomas Jones III

Capo Fret
9

♩=124

Intro

| A | A

Verse 1

(A)   **A**
Just take those old records off the shelf,

A
    I'll sit and listen to 'em by myself,   **D**

D   **E**
    Today's music ain't got the same soul,

E   **A**
    I like that old time rock 'n' roll.

A   **A**
    Don't try to take me to a disco,

A   **D**
    You'll never even get me out on the floor,

D   **E**
    In ten minutes I'll be late for the door,

E   **A** |**(A)**
    I like that old time rock 'n' roll.

Chorus 1

E |**A**
Still like that old time rock 'n' roll,

A   **D**
    That kind of music just soothes the soul,

D   **E**
    I reminisce about the days of old,

E   **A** |**(A) E** |
    With that old time rock 'n' roll.

Link 1

| A | A | D | D |
| E | E | A | **(A)** E |

Verse 2

Won't go to hear them play a tango,
I'd rather hear some blues or funky old soul,
There's only one sure way to get me to go,
Start playing old time rock 'n' roll.
Call me a relic, call me what you will,
Say I'm old-fashioned, say I'm over the hill,
Today's music ain't got the same soul,
I like that old time rock 'n' roll.

Chorus 2

As Chorus 1

Link 2

As Link 1

Chorus 3

As Chorus 1

Chorus 4

As Chorus 1 *(a capella, then repeat to fade)*

© COPYRIGHT 1983 MUSCLE SHOALS SOUND PUBLISHING, USA/PEERMUSIC III LIMITED
PEERMUSIC (UK) LIMITED.
ALL RIGHTS RESERVED. INTERNATIONAL COPYRIGHT SECURED.

Stage 1
Stage 2
Stage 3
Stage 4
Stage 5
Stage 6
Stage 7
Stage 8
Stage 9
Bonus

justinguitar.com

Stage 1
Stage 2
Stage 3
Stage 4
Stage 5
Stage 6
Stage 7
Stage 8
Stage 9
Bonus

 # Introduction

This track by Bob Seger is an awesome three-chord song for beginners, with a great message! To play along with the original recording you will need to put a capo right up at fret 9, which will make fretting the chord very difficult, but the original key is quite high, so I recommend you play it in open position which makes it easier to play and sing. Win, win!

 ## Strumming

Start as always by playing just four simple down-strums per bar—do this until you can play all the way through the song without any gaps between the chord changes.

Only then should you look at using other strumming patterns. The most appropriate pattern is probably even eighth-notes, played with an accent (louder strum) on beats 2 and 4. If you're an absolute beginner then don't worry about the accents too much at this stage—just enjoy the song, and maybe add these accents if you revisit the song a bit later.

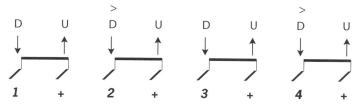

 ## End of the sequence

One thing to notice is the last bar of each chorus sequence (can you see that the chords are in an eight-bar sequence?) which is an E chord—the chord starts on the '+' after 1, so just resist changing to the E right away. Let the preceding A chord ring over the bar line (for half a beat) and then play even eighth-notes for the rest of the bar, on the E chord. If you are able to, start quietly and build it up—a classic rock technique!

Later in the course we learn a 'chunka-chunka' blues pattern (BC-183), which will sound great if you apply it to this song.

This Land Is Your Land

Words & Music by Woody Guthrie

Stage 1
Stage 2
Stage 3
Stage 4
Stage 5
Stage 6
Stage 7
Stage 8
Stage 9
Bonus

Capo Fret **5**

♩=100

Intro

```
| A   E | A      |
| D     | A    | E    | A           |
```
(This land is...)

Verse 1

            D   **A**
This land is your land, this land is my land
        E   **A**
From Cali - fornia to the New York island.
                D   **A**
From the red wood forest to the Gulf Stream waters
E   **A**   **A**
This land was made for you and me.   (As I went...)

Verse 2

As I went walking that ribbon of highway,
And I saw above me that endless skyway.
I saw below me that golden valley,
This land was made for you and me.

Link

```
‖: D     | A    | E    | A    :‖
```

Verse 3

I roamed and rambled and I followed my footsteps
To the sparkling sands of her diamond deserts.
All around me a voice was sounding:
This land was made for you and me.

Verse 4

There was a big high wall there that tried to stop me,
A sign was painted, said 'Private Property'.
But on the back side it didn't say nothing,
This land was made for you and me.

Verse 5

When the sun came shining, then I was strolling,
And the wheat fields waving and the dust clouds rolling,
A voice was chanting as the fog was lifting:
This land was made for you and me.

Verse 6

As Verse 1

Outro

```
‖: D     | A    | E    | A    :‖
```

© COPYRIGHT 1955 LUDLOW MUSIC INCORPORATED, USA.
TRO ESSEX MUSIC LIMITED.
ALL RIGHTS RESERVED. INTERNATIONAL COPYRIGHT SECURED.

Stage 1

Stage 2

Stage 3

Stage 4

Stage 5

Stage 6

Stage 7

Stage 8

Stage 9

Bonus

 # Introduction

This classic folk song from Woody Guthrie is an easy one for beginners but has room for some more complex playing too. There are many recorded versions of this song, often with slightly different lyrics and phrasing. We're looking at the version from the 'Asch Recordings'.

 ## In context

I need to point out a couple of things before we begin. Firstly, in order to keep the chords nice and simple, we need a capo on fret 5 to play along with the song. But the capo isn't essential, particularly if you're not playing along to the recording.

The second thing is that in this era of folk and blues music the concept of bars and consistent measures was quite flexible, so there are points in the original recording where Woody misses a beat or adds one—these are not mistakes, just choices, and because he's playing solo it makes no difference. I would recommend learning to play the song with a consistent rhythm, but the freedom to add or lose beats can often suit beginners!

 ## Strumming

Play the song through, using four simple down-strums to the bar, in order to get the chords under your fingers and to memorise the chord changes. Then move on to this strumming pattern below:

D		D	U	D		D	U
1	+	2	+	3	+	4	+

More advanced beginners might like to revisit this song after Stage 8 and play the bass note on beats 1 and 3 and a down- and up-strum in between, similar to the part played on the original recording.

The Tide Is High

Words & Music by John Holt, Howard Barrett & Tyrone Evans

Stage 1
Stage 2
Stage 3
Stage 4
Stage 5
Stage 6
Stage 7
Stage 8
Stage 9
Bonus

Capo Fret **2**

♩=96

Intro
‖: A | D E | A | D E :‖ *(Play x4)*

Chorus 1
A |D   E |
The tide is high but I'm holding on,
A |D   E |
I'm gonna be your number one.
A |D   E |
I'm not the kind of girl who gives up just like
A |D   E |
That, oh, no.

Verse 1
A |D   E |
It's not the things you do that tease and hurt me bad.
A |D   E |
But it's the way you do the things you do to me.
A |D   E |
I'm not the kind of girl who gives up just like
A |D   E |
That, oh, no.

Chorus 2
The tide is high but I'm holding on,
I'm gonna be your number one.
D   E   E
Number one.

Verse 2
Every girl wants you to be her man,
But I'll wait right here 'til it's my turn.
I'm not the kind of girl who gives up just like that, oh, no.

Chorus 3
The tide is high but I'm holding on,
I'm gonna be your number one.
D   E   D   E   E
Number one, Number one.

Link
‖: A | D E | A | D E :‖

Verse 3
As Verse 2

Chorus 4
As Chorus 3

Chorus 4
The tide is high but I'm holding on,
I'm gonna be your number one... *(Repeat to fade)*

© COPYRIGHT 1968 & 1972 CHESTER MUSIC LIMITED TRADING AS SPARTA FLORIDA MUSIC GROUP.
ALL RIGHTS RESERVED. INTERNATIONAL COPYRIGHT SECURED.

Stage 1
Stage 2
Stage 3
Stage 4
Stage 5
Stage 6
Stage 7
Stage 8
Stage 9
Bonus

 # Introduction

This Blondie hit (first performed by the Paragons) is a good song for beginners with a fun, reggae feel and easy chords.

 ## Chords & tuning

Please note that in the intro I've changed a couple of B minor chords to D chords. It's a relatively subtle difference and this only affects the intro. Also, If you want to play along with the original recording you'll probably want to tune it up about 20 cents (using software like *Transcribe!*) as the original tuning is a little flat.

Start by getting to grips with the chords and changes by just strumming four down-strums to the bar, making sure you start slowly. There shouldn't be any pauses between chord changes. Gradually work your way up to full tempo.

 ## Reggae strumming

Once you're confident with that, add the simple reggae-style strumming pattern, shown below. It's easy to get to grips with, as you'll just be playing on beats 2 and 4. As you progress you might like to try muting the chords (by touching the strings with your strumming hand) on beats 1 and 3.

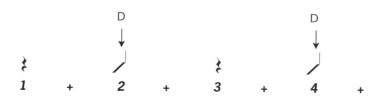

When Love Comes To Town

Words & Music by U2

♩=115

Intro

| E | E A | E | E A |
  Hey   yeah!   Hey   yeah!

Verse 1

E |E   A
I was a sailor, I was lost at sea,
  |E |E   A
I was under the waves before love rescued me.
E |E   A |
  I was a fighter, I could turn on a thread,
     E   (E)
Now I stand accused of the things I've said.

Chorus 1

     A   A
When love comes to town I'm gonna jump that train,
     E   E
When love comes to town I'm gonna catch that flame.
E   E
Maybe I was wrong to ever   let you down,
     E   (E)
But I did what I did before love came to town.

Link

| E | E A E | E A |

Verse 2

I used to make love under a red sunset
I was making promises I was soon to forget.
She was pale as the lace of her wedding gown
But I left her standing before love came to town.

Bridge

  A   A
I ran into a juke-joint when I heard a guitar scream
     E   E
The notes were turning blue, I was dazed and in a dream.
      E   E
As the music played I saw my life turn around
E   (E)
That was the day before love came to town.

Chorus 2   As Chorus 1

Link 2   ‖: E | E :‖ (Play x4)

Chorus 3   As Chorus 1

Link 3   ‖: E | E A :‖ (Play x6)

Verse 3

I was there when they crucified my Lord
I held the scabbard when the soldier drew his sword.
I threw the dice when they pierced his side
But I've seen love conquer the great divide.

Chorus 4   As Chorus 1

‖: E | E A :‖ (Play x6)

‖: A | A | E | E :‖ (Repeat to fade)

© COPYRIGHT 1988 BLUE MOUNTAIN MUSIC LIMITED.
ALL RIGHTS RESERVED. INTERNATIONAL COPYRIGHT SECURED.

Stage 1
Stage 2
Stage 3
Stage 4
Stage 5
Stage 6
Stage 7
Stage 8
Stage 9
Bonus

 # Introduction

This song was released by U2 and the great B.B King—it includes some superb playing from B.B., and I'm sure you'll enjoy playing along to it.

 Strumming

The main strumming part (played by The Edge) is a 2-bar loop—there are many variations of it throughout the song but this is a great starting point. You'll stay on the E chord until beat 3 of the second bar, and remember to lift up your chord grip on the '+' after 4, so that the open strings ring out.

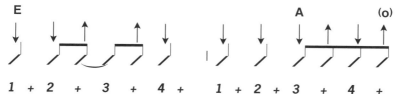

Be sure to notice when there are stops too—for these, you will play a chord on beat 1 and then remain silent for the next two bars.

Riff

The Edge's lead guitar part (played during 'Link 2') is based on an E chord, and uses his signature digital delay and reverb. I recommend playing this with a pick, making sure you follow the rhythm closely. Synchronising delay pedals can be tricky, so you're best off starting with just an electric guitar, a little gain on your amp and some reverb.

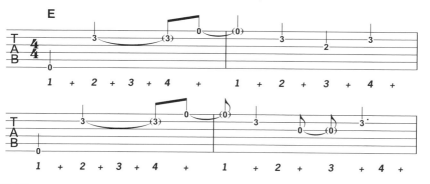

Stage 1

Stage 2

Stage 3

Stage 4

Stage 5

Stage 6

Stage 7

Stage 8

Stage 9

Bonus

STAGE 2 BC-121—BC-129

 ## Introduction

In Stage 2 we introduce three minor chords for you to learn.

You'll probably still be working on getting your strumming rhythm really solid, so again that should really be the focus of your attention. Try to play some songs along with a metronome, tapping your foot along at the same time (see BC-125 and BC-126).

Developing a strong sense of rhythm is one of the most important (and often-neglected) skills for any guitar player and the best ways to develop it are by practising tapping your foot along with the beat, and by playing along to a metronome. I would also recommend getting into the habit of tapping your foot along every time you hear music—make it something that happens naturally and it will always be there to help you!

Don't forget to keep revising some of the songs from the previous stage too. You will find it easier to apply your foot-tapping or metronome work to a song that you have already been working on, rather than applying it to a new one straight away.

To see the best improvement, you want a mix of some songs that you find easy—to build your confidence with—and some songs which push your technique and introduce new chord changes. It can be tricky to find the right balance. The easiest way to find it is to see what you enjoy! It's got to be fun; if you are spending too much time getting frustrated by harder songs, go back and consolidate your skills on the previous tunes before having a go at the new ones.

Be aware that all of the songs here have specific strumming patterns shown, but if you are just starting Stage 2, you should keep to playing four-strums-per-bar and tapping your foot. I have included more sophisticated patterns, so that as you develop your skills you can return to the song and make it sound more authentic, but it's very important that you just stick to the easy strumming while you develop your chord changes. I know it's hard, but be patient, and you'll get there sooner.

Stage 2 Chords

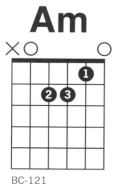

BC-121

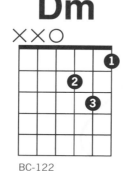

BC-122

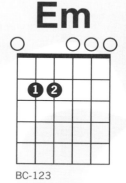

BC-123

 Strumming: tap your foot! BC-126

D		D		D		D	
1	+	2	+	3	+	4	+

Foot: Tap! Tap! Tap! Tap!

Stage 1
Stage 2
Stage 3
Stage 4
Stage 5
Stage 6
Stage 7
Stage 8
Stage 9
Bonus

505

Words & Music by Alex Turner

♩=140

Intro

‖: Dm | (Dm) | Em | (Em) :‖

Chorus 1

    Dm   (Dm)
I'm going back to five-o-five,
   Em (Em)   Dm   (Dm)
If it's a seven hour flight or a forty-five minute drive.
  Em   (Em)   Dm   (Dm)
In my imagi - nation you're waiting lying on your side
    Em   (Em) Dm (Dm) Em (Em)
With your hands between your thighs.

Verse 1

Dm   (Dm)
Stop and wait a sec,
     Em   (Em)   Dm   (Dm)
Oh, when you look at me like that my darling, what did you ex - pect?
 Em   (Em)   Dm   (Dm)
I probably still ad - ore you with your hands around my neck,
   Em   (Em) Dm (Dm) Em (Em)
Or I did last time I checked.

Verse 2

Not shy of a spark,
A knife twists at the thought that I should fall short of the mark.
Frightened by the bite though it's no harsher than the bark,
Middle of adventure, such a perfect place to start.

Chorus 2

As Chorus 1

Instr.

‖: Dm | (Dm) | Em | (Em) :‖ *(Play x4)*

Verse 3

But I crumble completely when you cry,
It seems like once again you've had to greet me with goodbye.
I'm always just about to go and spoil a surprise,
Take my hands off of your eyes too soon.

Chorus 3

As Chorus 1

Outro

‖: Dm | Dm | Em | Em :‖ *(Play x6)*

© COPYRIGHT 2007 EMI MUSIC PUBLISHING LIMITED.
ALL RIGHTS RESERVED. INTERNATIONAL COPYRIGHT SECURED.

Stage 1
Stage 2
Stage 3
Stage 4
Stage 5
Stage 6
Stage 7
Stage 8
Stage 9
Bonus

Introduction

I've often been asked if there are any great rock songs that just use two chords. To be honest, there wasn't much going until the Arctic Monkeys stormed it with this two-chord hit! This song was released on their second album, *Favourite Worst Nightmare* (2007).

 Chords

The whole song uses just Dm and Em chords and starts with a synth part that you can easily arrange for guitar—just strum the chords as shown once every two bars, letting the chords ring out. I've indicated this by putting every second chord in brackets.

It'll be easiest if you just to listen to the recording and play along—it will also be good practice to count out the beats in time with the recording, tapping your foot at the same time.

 Strumming

The rest of the band join in at Verse 3, resulting in a change of rhythm, but no change to the chords. At this point you'll launch into playing frantic down-strums on each eighth-note and it should feel very fast!

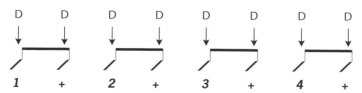

More advanced players might like to experiment with improvising over this track using the C Major scale. I'd also recommend trying to work out some of the lead lines from the original recording—learning songs and lead lines by ear is an essential skill for any serious guitarist and the sooner you start trying the better you'll get at it.

33

Business Time

Words & Music by Jermaine Atea Mahana Clement
& Bret Peter T McKenzie

♩=110

Verse sequence:

‖: **Am**   **Dm** | **Am** | **Am**   **Dm** | **Am**   **Dm**   **Em** |

Verse 1

Ah yeah, that's right baby. Girl, tonight we're gonna make love.
You know how I know baby? Because it's Wednesday
And Wednesday night is the night that we make love.
Tuesday night is the night that we go and visit your mother
But Wednesday night is the night that we make love.
Because everything is just right, conditions are perfect.
There's nothing good on TV, conditions are perfect.
You turn to me and say something sexy like,
'I might go to bed, I've got work in the morning.'
I know what youre trying to say, baby,
Youre trying to say, 'Oh, yeah, it's business time, it's business time.'

Chorus 1

Dm   **Em**   **Am**
  It's business,   it's business time, that's what you're trying to say,
                                         Am
You're trying to say let's get down to business, it's business time,
Dm   **Em**   **Am**   **Am**
  It's business,   it's business time,   ooh.

Verse 2

Next thing you know we're in the bathroom brushing our teeth
Thats all part of it, that's foreplay.
Then you go sort out the recycling,
That's not part of it but it's still very important.
Then we're are in the bedroom,
You're wearing that old ugly, baggy T-shirt
From that team-building exercise you did for your old work
And it's never looked better on you, ooh,
Team-building exercise not denied,
Oh, you don't know what you're doing to me.
I remove my jeans but trip over them because I've still got my shoes on
But then I turn it into a sexy dance.
Next thing you know I'm down to just my socks
And you know when I'm down to just my socks what time it is
It's time for business, It's business time.

Chorus 2

It's business, it's business time,
You know when I'm down to just my socks it's time for business
That's why they're called business socks.
It's business, it's business time.

Verse 3

Making love, making love for two, making love for two minutes,
When it's with me, you only need two minutes 'cause I'm so intense,
Two minutes in heaven is better than one minute in heaven.
You say something sexy like, 'Is that it?'
I know what youre trying to say,
You're trying to say, 'Oh yeah, that's it'
And you tell me you want some more
Well, I'm not surprised but I am quite sleepy.

© COPYRIGHT 2008 BMG MONARCH.
CHRYSALIS MUSIC LIMITED.
ALL RIGHTS RESERVED. INTERNATIONAL COPYRIGHT SECURED.

Stage 1
Stage 2
Stage 3
Stage 4
Stage 5
Stage 6
Stage 7
Stage 8
Stage 9
Bonus

Stage 1
Stage 2
Stage 3
Stage 4
Stage 5
Stage 6
Stage 7
Stage 8
Stage 9
Bonus

Chorus 3   It's business, it's business time,
Business hours are over, baby,
It's business, it's business time.

 ## Introduction

I'm a huge fan of the Flight Of The Conchords and although the song uses barre chords, you can just about recreate it using Am, Dm and Em. To play along with the recording you'll need a capo on fret 10, which gets very cramped, so I recommend playing without one—it'll just make the key one tone higher. We're looking at the live video of this song, available on YouTube.

 ## Basic pattern

The basic pattern for the verse is a four-bar loop. In bars 1 and 3, the Dm chord is only played on beat 4, and in bar 4, the Dm and Em are just a beat each on beats 3 and 4—see the pattern below.

Am			Dm	Am		Dm	Em
↓	↓	↓	↓	↓	↓	↓	↓

1   +   2   +   3   +   4   +   1   +   2   +   3   +   4   +

Because the lyrics are so free and rhythmically loose this can be a hard song to play and sing at the same time. The upside is that you can be pretty loose with the chord changes and with how many beats you stay on a particular chord—just keep the beat, as that's most important!

Funk strumming

Proper funk strumming can be difficult, so try this intermediate strumming pattern. It uses all down- strums, and the idea is that you play the chord, and immediately afterwards mute all the strings with the outside of your strumming hand—it can be quite tricky but it's fun.

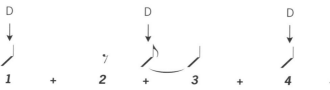

D		D		D
↓		↓		↓

1   +   2   +   3   +   4   +

Stage 1
Stage 2
Stage 3
Stage 4
Stage 5
Stage 6
Stage 7
Stage 8
Stage 9
Bonus

Chocolate Jesus

Words & Music by Tom Waits & Kathleen Brennan

Capo Fret **6**

♩=102

Intro

| Am | Am | Am | Dm |
| Dm | Am | E | Am |

Verse 1

      Am   **Am**
Well, I don't go to church on Sunday,
Am   **Dm**
Don't get on my knees to pray,
       Dm   **Am**
Don't memorize the books of the Bible,
  E   **E**
I got my own special way.
Am   **Am**
I know Jesus loves me,
Am   **Dm**
Maybe just a little bit more,
  Dm   **Am**
I fall down on my knees every Sunday,
    E   **Am**
At Zerelda Lee's candy store.

Chorus 1

      Am   **Am** **Am**   **Dm**
Well it's got to be a chocolate Jesus, make me feel good inside.
Dm   **Am** **E**   **Am**
Got to be a chocolate Jesus, keep me satisfied.

Verse 2

Well I don't want no Abba-Zaba, don't want no Almond Joy,
There ain't nothing better, suitable for this boy.
Well it's the only thing that can pick me up,
Better than a cup of gold,
See only a chocolate Jesus can satisfy my soul.

Instrumental

Am	Am	Am	Dm
Dm	Am	E	E
Am	Am	Am	Dm
Dm	Am	E	Am

Bridge

        Dm   **Dm**
When the weather gets rough and it's whiskey in the shade,
    Dm   **Am**
It's best to wrap your saviour up in cellophane.
    Dm   **Dm**
He flows like the big muddy but that's ok,
E   **E**   **E**
Pour him over ice cream for a nice parfait.

© COPYRIGHT 1999 JALMA MUSIC.
UNIVERSAL MUSIC PUBLISHING MGB LIMITED.
ALL RIGHTS RESERVED. INTERNATIONAL COPYRIGHT SECURED.

justinguitar.com

Stage 1
Stage 2
Stage 3
Stage 4
Stage 5
Stage 6
Stage 7
Stage 8
Stage 9
Bonus

Chorus 2	Well it's got to be a chocolate Jesus, good enough for me, Got to be a chocolate Jesus, it's good enough for me.
Chorus 3	As Chorus 1
Outro	As Intro, then: | E | Am | E | Am |

Introduction

Tom Waits is one of my favourite songwriters but not much of his work is suitable for beginners. Fortunately this 8-bar minor blues is perfect for Stage 2 of our course. The recording (from *Mule Variations*) is very sparse with minimal instrumentation, just the thud of an upright bass, a tambourine and some banjo plinking away, but it works great on guitar too.

Find the beat

If you're trying to find the beat of the song, you'll hear a tambourine being played on beats 2 and 4—this should help you get your bearings. Start by just playing four down-strums to the bar and get used to where the chord changes are. Many people struggle initially with Dm and you might find it easier to use finger 4 on string 2. The Am to E is a nice easy change, so it's just that Dm that might cause you problems—but nothing a bit of practice won't solve!

Strumming

Once you're confident with the chord changes, try using this strumming pattern shown below—putting a slightly harder strum on beats 2 and 4 will help emphasise the groove.

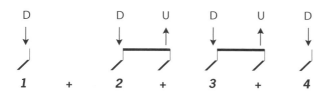

Christine's Tune (Devil In Disguise)

Words & Music by Gram Parsons & Chris Hillman

Stage 1
Stage 2
Stage 3
Stage 4
Stage 5
Stage 6
Stage 7
Stage 8
Stage 9
Bonus

Capo Fret **6**

♩=198

Intro ‖: E |D A |E |D A   :‖

Chorus 1
(A)   D   E   D   A
She's a devil in dis - guise,   You can see it in her eyes.
         A   E   E   D   A   A   E   E
She's telling dirty lies,   She's a devil in dis - guise, in dis - guise.

Verse 1
            E   A   E   E
Now, a woman like that all she does is hate you,
            E   A   E   E
She doesn't know what makes a man a man.
            E   A   E   E
She'll talk about the time that she's been with you,
            A   A   E   E
She'll speak your name to everyone she can.

Chorus 2
(E)   D   E   E   D   A   A
She's a devil in dis - guise,   You can see it in her eyes.
         A   E   E
She's telling dirty lies,
            D   A   A   E |D A|
She's a devil in dis - guise,   in dis - guise.

Instr. 1 |: E |E |E |E |
              |E |D A |E |E |

Verse 2
Unhappiness has been her close companion,
Her world is full of jealously and doubt.
It gets her off to see a person crying,
She's just the kind that you can do without.

Chorus 3 As Chorus 2

Instr. 2 As Instr. 1

Verse 3
Her number always turns up in your pocket
Whenever you are looking for a dime.
It's all right to call her, but I'll bet you,
The moon is full and you're just wasting time.

Chorus 4 As Chorus 2

            E |D A |E |D A |E |D A |
In dis - guise,   in dis - guise,   in dis - guise.

Outro ‖: E |E |E |E   :‖

Repeat and fade

© COPYRIGHT 1969 IRVING MUSIC.
RONDOR INTERNATIONAL INC.
ALL RIGHTS RESERVED. INTERNATIONAL COPYRIGHT SECURED.

38

Stage 1
Stage 2
Stage 3
Stage 4
Stage 5
Stage 6
Stage 7
Stage 8
Stage 9
Bonus

Introduction

This country-rock song from The Flying Burrito Brothers is an interesting take on the three-chord trick. It looks easy at first glance but because of the speed of the chord changes and the phrasing of the lyrics it can be a little tricky for beginners—but it's still great fun and there's a lot to learn from sticking with it.

Strumming

To start with, play just four down-strums to the bar—they'll still be quite fast but you'll need to be confident with that before trying other things! You'll find one of the quirks of the song is how long it stays on certain chords, particularly in the chorus, so you want to get familiar with that while you're still on the easy strumming. Once you feel happy with that, you can apply 'Old Faithful' (page 19) which will work well.

A more authentic strumming pattern would be to play even eighth-notes with a heavy accent on beats 2 and 4. This means that you will strum every down- and up-beat in the bar but you'll heavily accent beats 2 and 4. It's a very specific feel which is likely to take you some practice—especially if you want to sing over it.

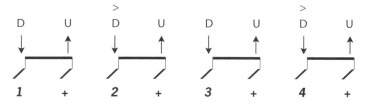

As well as the main strumming patterns you'll need to listen out for places where the whole group pick up on certain accents. There's an obvious one during the intro (and repeated at the end of the choruses) shown below with the A being played on the '+' after beat 2, but others you'll have to pick up by ear!

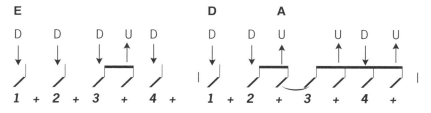

Stage 1

Stage 2

Stage 3

Stage 4

Stage 5

Stage 6

Stage 7

Stage 8

Stage 9

Bonus

Desire

Words by Bono, Music by U2

♩=216

Intro

E
    Yeah.

riff

‖: D   A   E | A   E | D   A   E | A   E   :‖

Verse 1

(with riff x4)
Lover, I'm on the street,
Gonna go where the bright lights and the big city meet

Chorus

(A)   **(E)**   **D**   **D**   **A**   **A**
With a red gui - tar   on fire,

     (with riff x2)
De - sire.

Verse 2

(with riff x8)
She's a candle burning in my room,
I'm like the needle, needle and spoon.
Over the counter with a shotgun, pretty soon everybody got one.

Chorus

And the fever when I'm beside her,
Desire. (*x2*)

Link 1

| **(E)** | **(E)** | **(E)** | **(E)** |

Chorus

And the fever, getting higher,
Desire. (*x2*)

Bridge

D   **D**   **A**   **A**
Burn - ing.

D   **D**   **E**   **E**   **E**
Burn - ing.

Link 2

(riff x4)

Verse 3

(with riff x10)
She's the dollars, she's my protection,
Yeah, she's a promise in the year of election
Oh sister, I can't let you go,
Like a preacher stealing hearts at a travelling show
For love or money, money, money, money, money, money,
Money, money, money, money, money.

Chorus

And the fever, getting higher,
Desire. (*x4*)

Solo

(riff x4)

Outro

Desire. (*x2*)

© COPYRIGHT 1988 BLUE MOUNTAIN MUSIC LIMITED.
ALL RIGHTS RESERVED. INTERNATIONAL COPYRIGHT SECURED.

Stage 1
Stage 2
Stage 3
Stage 4
Stage 5
Stage 6
Stage 7
Stage 8
Stage 9
Bonus

 Introduction

This three-chord wonder featured on *Rattle And Hum*, U2's album and film from 1988.

Fast changes

This song only uses three chords, but it's pretty fast, so it's a great one for working on those quick chord changes. To play along with the original you will need to tune down one semitone, and the easiest way to tune down is to use a tuner to tune your strings to the notes E♭, A♭, D♭, G♭, B♭ and E♭ (from thick to thin). Another easy way to do this is to place the capo on the 1st fret, tune your guitar in standard tuning, and then remove the capo!

Once you have learnt your sus chords you might like to revisit this song; listen to the original recording and try to add some A and D sus chords like The Edge does.

 Strumming

The strumming for the main pattern is quite specific; although it's a little tricky it sounds great! With all these types of pattern-based riffs you MUST start slowly and gradually work the tempo up.

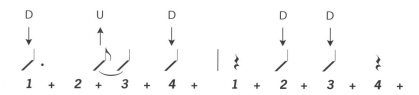

Stage 1
Stage 2
Stage 3
Stage 4
Stage 5
Stage 6
Stage 7
Stage 8
Stage 9
Bonus

Don't Let Me Down

Words & Music by John Lennon & Paul McCartney

Capo Fret 2

♩=76

Intro

| D | D | |

Chorus 1

               Em   Em
Don't let me down,
               D   D
Don't let me down,
               Em   Em
Don't let me down,
               D   D
Don't let me down.

Verse 1

N.C.   Em
Nobody ever loved me like she does,
           Em   D   D
Ooh she does, yes she does,
N.C.   Em
And if somebody loved me like she do me,
           Em   D   D
Ooh she do me, yes she does.

Chorus 2

As Chorus 1

Bridge 1

N.C.   D   D
I'm in love for the first time,
                             A   A
Don't you know it's going to last.
                        A   A
It's a love that lasts forever,
                      D   D
It's a love that has no past.

Chorus 3

As Chorus 1

Verse 2

And from the first time that she really done me,
Ooh, she done me, she done me good.
I guess nobody ever really done me,
Ooh she done me, she done me good.

Chorus 4

As Chorus 1

Chorus 5

As Chorus 1 *(vocals ad lib.)*

© COPYRIGHT 1969 SONY/ATV MUSIC PUBLISHING.
ALL RIGHTS RESERVED. INTERNATIONAL COPYRIGHT SECURED

Introduction

This classic Beatles song (released in 1969 as a 'double A-side') is a great singalong number, and has enough quirks to keep it interesting, even though the chords are very simple. We're playing it with a capo on the 2nd fret.

 Getting started

I recommend starting with four down-strums to the bar and getting used to the structure—and you'll need to because there are 5/4 bars lurking (bars with 5 beats in them instead of 4). They're easy to spot because they happen during the stops in the verses, where N.C is written (it means 'No Chord'). During the stops, you'll count to 5, not the usual 4 (but not in the bridge).

 Strumming

The beginner's option for this song is to play even eighth-note down-strums:

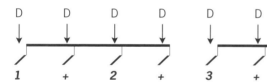

If you want more of a challenge then try the patterns below. Notice that we've divided each beat into 4, rather than 2. They are not beginner strumming patterns, and might be best to revisit later in your studies.

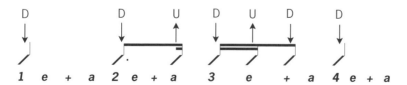

There are several 'hits' and accents that the whole band play—these are best learnt by listening, but here are the chorus accents.

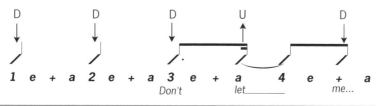

Stage 1
Stage 2
Stage 3
Stage 4
Stage 5
Stage 6
Stage 7
Stage 8
Stage 9
Bonus

Moves Like Jagger

Words & Music by Adam Levine, Benjamin Levin, Shellback & Ammar Malik

Capo Fret 2

♩=128

Sequence throughout:

| Am(7) | Am(7) | Am(7) | Am(7) |

| Dm(7) | Dm(7) | Dm(7) | Dm(7) |

Intro   Sequence x1

Verse 1
Just shoot for the stars if it feels right,
And aim for my heart if you feel like.
And take me away and make it O.K.,
I swear I'll behave.

You wanted control, so we waited,
I put on a show, now and make it.
You say I'm a kid, my ego is big,
I don't give a ****, and it goes like this...

Chorus 1
Take me by the tongue and I'll know you,
Kiss me till you're drunk and I'll show you
All the moves like Jagger,
I've got the moves like Jagger,
I've got the moves like Jagger.

I don't need to try to control you,
Look into my eyes and I'll own you
With the moves like Jagger,
I've got the moves like Jagger,
I've got the moves like Jagger.

Verse 2
Maybe it's hard when you feel like
You're broken and scarred, nothing feels right
But when you're with me I'll make you believe
That I've got the key.

Oh, so get in the car, we can ride it
Wherever you want, get inside it
And you want to steer but I'm shifting gears
I'll take it from here, oh yeah, yeah, and it goes like this...

Chorus 2   As Chorus 1

Bridge
You wanna know how to make me smile,
Take control, own me just for the night.
And if I share my secret, you're gonna have to keep it,
Nobody else can see this.

© COPYRIGHT 2011 UNIVERSAL MUSIC CAREERS/MATZA BALL MUSIC/WHERE DA KASZ AT/
SUDGEE MUSIC/MARU CHA CHA/MXM MUSIC AB.
KOBALT MUSIC PUBLISHING LIMITED/UNIVERSAL/MCA MUSIC LIMITED/UNIVERSAL MUSIC PUBLISHING MGB LIMITED.
ALL RIGHTS RESERVED. INTERNATIONAL COPYRIGHT SECURED.

Stage 1
Stage 2
Stage 3
Stage 4
Stage 5
Stage 6
Stage 7
Stage 8
Stage 9
Bonus

cont.

So watch and learn, I won't show you twice,
Head to toe, oh baby rub me right.
But if I share my secret, you're gonna have to keep it,
Nobody else can see this, eh, eh, eh, yeah, and it goes like this...

Chorus 3   As Chorus 1

 # Introduction

Maroon 5 are an incredible band, and are seriously great musicians—this is one of their signature tunes.

 # Easy strumming

The funky feel of the rhythm guitar is quite complex, but we can simplify the rhythm and have just as much fun with it. Start with a simple Am chord, and play four down-strums to the bar, for four bars. Then change to Dm and do the same thing. Play this along with the recording. The trick is to get your chord transitions as smooth as possible, with no pause as you change chords.

Once you've nailed that, we'll try a slightly more involved strumming pattern. If you've not met it before, I call this pattern 'Old Faithful' because it works well in many different contexts.

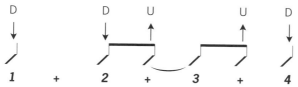

Chord extensions

The more adventurous among you might like to try changing the chords to Am7 and Dm7, shown below—they're a little more complex but will sound closer to the guitar on the original recording.

Am7

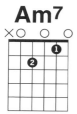

Dm7

Stir It Up

Words & Music by Bob Marley

♩=156

Stage 1
Stage 2
Stage 3
Stage 4
Stage 5
Stage 6
Stage 7
Stage 8
Stage 9
Bonus

Intro

‖: A | A | D | E   :‖   *(Play x4)*

Chorus 1

```
A          A      D    E
Stir it up,        little darlin',
A          A         D    E
Stir it up,    c'mon baby,   c'mon and
A          A    D    E
Stir it up,        little darlin'.
A          A    D   E
Stir it up.
```

Verse 1

```
              A           A
It's been a long, long time
D         E              A    A    D    E
   Since I've got you on my mind.
      A              A      D    E
And now you are here,   I said it's so clear,
      A              A
To see what we could do, baby,
D            E
   Just me and you, come on and
```

Chorus 2   As Chorus 1

Verse 2

I'll push the wood, then I'll raise your fire,
Then I'll satisfy your heart's desire.
I will stir it every, every minute,
All you've got to do, baby,
Is keep it in it.

Chorus 3   As Chorus 1

Verse 3

Quench me when I'm thirsty,
Cool me down baby when I'm hot,
Your recipe, darlin', is so tasty
When you show and stir your pot.

Chorus 4   As Chorus 1

Link   ‖: A | A | D | E   :‖   *Repeat ad lib.*

Chorus 5   As Chorus 4   *Repeat to fade*

© COPYRIGHT 1973 FIFTY-SIX HOPE ROAD MUSIC LIMITED/BLACKWELL FULLER MUSIC PUBLISHING LIMITED.
BLUE MOUNTAIN MUSIC LIMITED.
ALL RIGHTS RESERVED. INTERNATIONAL COPYRIGHT SECURED

Introduction

This classic Bob Marley & The Wailers song is great fun to play for beginners.

Strumming

Start by playing four down-strums per bar, and get familiar with the song structure. Play along with the original recording if you can, and make sure there are not long gaps between your chord changes.

To play in a more authentic, reggae style, play a down-strum on beat 2 and an up-strum immediately after it, on the '+'. Then do the same on beat 4. The original uses very heavily muted barre chords, but we can still get a reggae groove going by using beginner chords. Use the outside of your strumming hand to mute all the strings on beats 1 and 3 to get a short, 'clipped' effect.

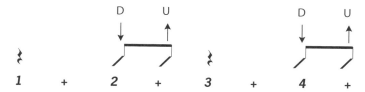

Chords

More advanced players (i.e. not beginners) might like to try using the chord grips below, which are mini-barre chords. Use the strumming as shown above but press the chord very lightly so the notes don't ring out properly—they should sound dead and muted. It's all about how much pressure you hold the chord down with, so listen to the original and see how close you can get to the tone.

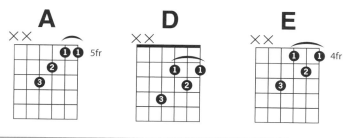

Stage 1
Stage 2
Stage 3
Stage 4
Stage 5
Stage 6
Stage 7
Stage 8
Stage 9
Bonus

Stage 1
Stage 2
Stage 3
Stage 4
Stage 5
Stage 6
Stage 7
Stage 8
Stage 9
Bonus

Use Me

Words & Music by Bill Withers

$\quad\bullet=156$

Chord sequence throughout:

| Em(7) | Em(7) | A(7) | A(7) | |

Em7

A7

Intro

Play sequence *(x2)*

Verse 1

My friends feel it's their appointed duty,
They keep trying to tell me
All you want to do is use me.
But my answer, yeah to all that use me stuff,
I want to spread the news
That if it feels this good getting used,
Oh, you just keep on using me
Until you use me up,
Until you use me up.

Verse 2

My brother sit me right down and he talked to me,
He told me that I ought not to let you just walk on me.
And I'm sure he meant well,
Yeah, but when our talk was through
I said, brother, if you only knew
You'd wish that you were in my shoes.
You just keep on using me,
Until you use me up,
Until you use me up.

Verse 3

Sometimes, it's true you really do abuse me,
You get me in a crowd of high-class people
And then you act real rude to me.
But, oh, baby, baby, baby, baby,
When you love me, I can't get enough.
I want to spread the news
That if it feels this good getting used,
Girl, you just keep on using me
Until you use me up,
Until you use me up.

Outro

Talking 'bout you using people,
It all depends on what you do.
It ain't too bad the way you're using me,
'Cause I sure am using you to do the things you do,
To do the things you do.

© COPYRIGHT 1972 INTERIOR MUSIC CORPORATION, USA.
UNIVERSAL/MCA MUSIC LIMITED.
ALL RIGHTS RESERVED. INTERNATIONAL COPYRIGHT SECURED.

Stage 1

Stage 2

Stage 3

Stage 4

Stage 5

Stage 6

Stage 7

Stage 8

Stage 9

Bonus

Introduction

This funky Bill Withers tune is an easy song for beginners, and more advanced players can have some fun with the original chord grips.

Strumming

We're going to look at a few ways to play this song—there are just two bars of each chord (Em and A), although there are a few 'stops' that you can copy from the arrangement if you want to. As we're at an early stage in the course, we can simplify the chords to just Em and A, starting off by playing four simple down-strums to the bar. Play this along with the recording, and have some fun!

To make the rhythm a bit more exciting, you can play even eighth-notes, using down- and up-strums. Try to make it feel groovy, and not too stiff!

Chord extensions

Next up you might like to add the '7' to the chords, which will give the song a nice funky feel (see the chord diagrams on the song sheet).

And if you want to get really funky, the actual chords that Bill Withers used are shown below—though they're not for beginners!

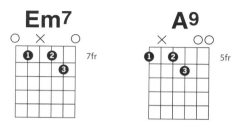

To add another even funkier level you can start lifting the chord a little so that you get a muted hit on some strums. You'll witness Bill Withers using this technique on a live video on YouTube (the one where he's wearing a fetching orange roll neck sweater).

You Don't Love Me (No, No, No)

Words & Music by Ellas McDaniel, Willie Cobbs, Euwart Beckford & Duke Reid

♩=162

Intro

N.C.
We're in town to tell the people 'bout the million things coming your way.

| D | D | D | D | |

Verse 1

      D **D**   **D**   **Am**   **Am** **Am**
No, no, no,   you don't love me and I know now.
      D **D**   **Am**   **Am** **Am** **Am**
No, no, no,   you don't love me yes I know now.
       E   **E**   **D**   **D**   **Am**   **Am**
'Cause you left me, baby,   and I've got no place to go now.

Link

| Am | Am | |

Verse 2

No, no, no, I'll do anything you say boy.
No, no, no, I'll do anything you say boy.
'Cause if you ask me, baby, I'll get on my knees and pray, boy.

Link

| Am | Am | |

Instr.

| D | D | Am | Am | |

| D | D | Am | Am | |

Verse 3

     D **D**   **D**   **Am**   **Am** **Am**
No, no, no, you don't love me and I know now.
     D **D**   **Am**   **Am** **Am**
No, no, no,   you don't love me yes I know now.

(Repeat Verse to fade)

© COPYRIGHT 1967 & 1994 EMBASSY MUSIC CORPORATION/KATRINA MUSIC COMPANY
CARLIN MUSIC CORPORATION.
ALL RIGHTS RESERVED. INTERNATIONAL COPYRIGHT SECURED.

Stage 1
Stage 2
Stage 3
Stage 4
Stage 5
Stage 6
Stage 7
Stage 8
Stage 9
Bonus

 Introduction

This infectious song uses just three basic chords but has a cool reggae rhythm, which makes it groove, and is really satisfying to play. There are many versions of this song—we're looking at Dawn Penn's later recording from 1994. You're possibly best off ignoring the intro, which is difficult to recreate on guitar!

Chips

As usual, start by playing four down-strums per bar—just to get familiar with the song structure and the chord changes. Watch out because there are a few chord changes that are in non-instinctive places—we're used to feeling groups of 4, 8, 12 or 16 bars, but this song has a few changes after just 3 bars, which can feel odd.

When you listen to the recording you'll clearly hear the guitar playing short 'chips' on the off beats (shown by a '+'). It's an easy mistake to think they are on the beat, but they're between the beats, as is the case in pretty much every reggae song ever! Off beats are usually played as up-strums, but somehow the down-strums 'feel' better here.

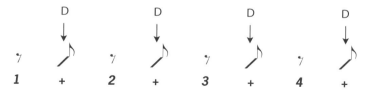

Muting

Try muting the strings with your strumming hand on the beat, shown below with an X. Use the side of your strumming hand to mute all the strings, then lift off and play the chord with a down-strum and then mute again, continuing this process. Your hand should feel like it's bouncing, and it should help you keep the beat grooving—and don't forget to keep your foot tapping on the beat!

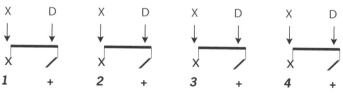

Stage 1
Stage 2
Stage 3
Stage 4
Stage 5
Stage 6
Stage 7
Stage 8
Stage 9
Bonus

51

Stage 1

Stage 2

Stage 3

Stage 4

Stage 5

Stage 6

Stage 7

Stage 8

Stage 9

Bonus

STAGE 3 BC-131—BC-139

 Introduction

We introduce a couple of new chords in this stage which require a bit of a stretch, and which many people find tricky to change between at first. This is perfectly normal so don't worry about it. Getting these chords right is just down to practice; I suggest doing lots of One-Minute Changes (BC-134) to help you improve.

We're also introducing several new strumming patterns for you to incorporate into your playing. You will need to practise each of these patterns on a single chord so much that it becomes automatic for you when you want to use it in a song.

This is VERY important. The students who progress the fastest are those that separate their work on chord changes from their work on rhythm patterns. So, keep using the 'boring' four-strums-per bar for songs to really nail the chord changes, while working separately on rhythm patterns, strumming on a single chord until they become instinctive. Then, you can play the chord changes using the new strumming patterns, as you will be comfortable with both.

Another trick is to mute all the strings with your fretting hand and then practise strumming along with the original recording. This takes away the anxiety of the chord changes and allows you to focus on the most important aspect: the rhythm. It will really help you pick up the groove, and once you feel comfortable with it, you'll find it easier to pop the chords in!

In fact, you should only start using the rhythm patterns once you can play through a song with four-strums-per-bar using a metronome, without stopping for any of the chord changes. It requires patience, but really works. I hope you have more patience than I did when I was learning!

Some songs in this stage are shown with a strumming pattern that uses a tie. We've already looked at the strumming pattern 'Old Faithful' (which hopefully will become one of your most dependable strumming patterns), which uses a tie crossing over the barline, so it's not entirely new to you. You will notice that using ties and off beats in your strumming will often sound a lot more natural than the standard four-to-the-bar strumming—but you're not going to rush into it things before you're ready are you?

 Stage 3 Chords

G

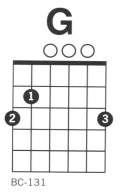

BC-131

C

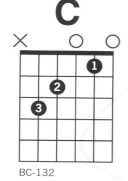

BC-132

 Stage 3: Your notes

Stage 1
Stage 2
Stage 3
Stage 4
Stage 5
Stage 6
Stage 7
Stage 8
Stage 9
Bonus

Down On The Corner

Words & Music by John C. Fogerty

Capo Fret
3

♩=108

Intro	`| A	E A	A	E A |` `| D	A	A	E A |`

Verse 1

```
A                       |E               A  |
Early in the evenin' just about supper time,
A                            |E                   A  |
Over by the courthouse they're starting to un - wind.
D                    A
Four kids on the corner trying to bring you up.
A                        |E              A  |
Willy picks a tune out and he blows it on the harp.
```

Chorus 1

```
|D          A    |E      A
Down on the corner, out in the street
         |D            A
Willy and the Poorboys are playin'
   |E             A    |
Bring a nickel; tap your feet.
```

Verse 2

Rooster hits the washboard and people just got to smile,
Blinky thumps the gut bass and solos for a while.
Poorboy twangs the rhythm out on his kalamazoo.
Willy goes into a dance and doubles on kazoo.

Chorus 2   As Chorus 1

Link 1

```
| A     | E  A | A       | E   A |
| D     | A    | A       | E   A |
```

Chorus 3   As Chorus 1

Link 2

```
| A     | E  A | A       | E   A |
```

Verse 3

You don't need a penny just to hang around,
But if you've got a nickel, won't you lay your money down?
Over on the corner there's a happy noise.
People come from all around to watch the magic boy.

Chorus 4   As Chorus 1 *(Play x4 to fade)*

© COPYRIGHT 1969 JONDORA MUSIC INCORPORATED.
PRESTIGE MUSIC LIMITED.
ALL RIGHTS RESERVED. INTERNATIONAL COPYRIGHT SECURED.

Stage 1
Stage 2
Stage 3
Stage 4
Stage 5
Stage 6
Stage 7
Stage 8
Stage 9
Bonus

justinguitar.com

Stage 1
Stage 2
Stage 3
Stage 4
Stage 5
Stage 6
Stage 7
Stage 8
Stage 9
Bonus

 ## Introduction

Creedence Clearwater Revival are one of my favourite bands of all time, and this song suits both beginner and intermediate players really well.

Strumming and riff

Start by playing four down-strums per bar, and try playing along with the recording, getting used to the structure and chord changes. Then have a go at the simplified strumming pattern shown below.

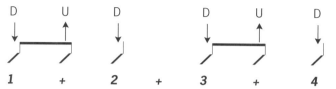

The guitar riff isn't hard to play. You can learn it by counting out the rhythm, or just listening and copying, or a combination of the two! Take it slowly and don't worry about fingering—just get stuck in!

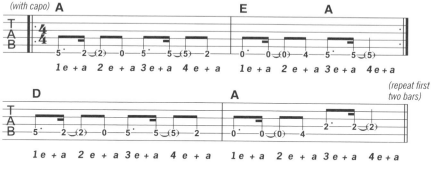

Advanced strumming

The 'authentic' strumming pattern is quite a challenge, and not for beginners. When there are two chords per bar you will change to the second chord on the beat '2a'.

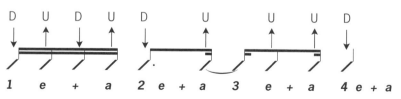

Get Lucky

Words & Music by Thomas Bangalter, Pharrell Williams,
Guy-Manuel de Homem-Christo & Nile Rodgers

Capo
Fret
2

♩=116

> **Chord sequence throughout**
>
> | Am | C | Em | D |

Intro　Play sequence (x4)

Verse 1

(seq x2)
Like the legend of the Phoenix
All ends with beginnings,
What keeps the planet spinning, uh huh,
The force from the beginning.

Pre-chorus 1

(seq x2)
We've come too far
To give up who we are.
So let's raise the bar
And our cups to the stars.

Chorus 1

(seq x2)
She's up all night to the sun,
I'm up all night to get some,
She's up all night for good fun,
I'm up all night to get lucky.
We're up all night to the sun,
We're up all night to get some,
We're up all night for good fun,
We're up all night to get lucky (x5)

Link 1　Play sequence

Verse 2
The present has no ribbon,
Your gift keps on giving,
What is this I'm feeling?
If you wanna leave, I'm ready, ah.

Pre-chorus 2　As Pre-chorus 1

Chorus 2　As Chorus 1

Bridge 1　Play sequence x4 (w/synth vox. ad lib.)

Pre-chorus 3　As Pre-chorus 1

Chorus 3　As Chorus 1

Bridge 2　...we're up all night to get lucky (x4)

Outro　*Repeat sequence to fade*

© COPYRIGHT 2013 EMI APRIL MUSIC INC/MORE WATER FROM NAZARETH PUBLISHING INC./IMAGEM CV/XLC MUSIC.
IMAGEM MUSIC/SONY/ATV MUSIC PUBLISHING LIMITED/EMI MUSIC PUBLISHING LIMITED.
ALL RIGHTS RESERVED. INTERNATIONAL COPYRIGHT SECURED.

justinguitar.com

Stage 1
Stage 2
Stage 3
Stage 4
Stage 5
Stage 6
Stage 7
Stage 8
Stage 9
Bonus

Introduction

What a killer groove! This song, released by Daft Punk in 2013, features one of the greatest funk guitar players of all time: Nile Rodgers.

Easy strumming

This song is all about the funky groove and it uses the same four chords for the entire song. To keep it simple for beginners I'm showing you a version using a capo (on fret 2) and open chords, alongside easy strumming, but I'll dig a little deeper as you progress and get to know the song. If you're a beginner, I'd recommend using 'Old Faithful' (see page 19), especially for an acoustic vibe at a party!

Strumming sixteenth-notes

If you want to pick up the funk you'll need to strum twice as fast, playing sixteenth-notes instead of eighth-notes (this is covered in detail in my *Intermediate Method*). This isn't much harder, it just requires more strums. There are a lot of subtleties to funk strumming (I have a whole module on it on my website) but to start you off, it's all about accents!

Strum on every sixteenth-note (as shown below) but slightly lift the chord so you get a muted note rather than a clear chord on each strum. You should focus the strums more on the thin strings—this is crucial to getting a bright, funky tone. Then, following the pattern below, pressing the chord down where the accents (>) are shown.

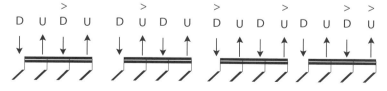

Funk strumming takes a lot of work, but this track is ideal as an introduction. Listen and try to emulate the guitar groove. You won't learn it by thinking, but you will by listening and copying! Once you've learnt your barre chords, I'd strongly recommend coming back to this song, as you'll then find it much easier to recreate the 'clipped' funky style.

If You Wanna

Words & Music by Arni Arnason, Freddie Cowan,
Peter Robertson & Justin Hayward-Young

Stage 1
Stage 2
Stage 3
Stage 4
Stage 5
Stage 6
Stage 7
Stage 8
Stage 9
Bonus

♩=166

Intro   ‖: D | D | D | D   :‖   *Play x3*

Verse 1
     D   D
Well I don't want to wake up in the morning
        D   D
But I've got to face the day.
G   A   G   D   D
That's what all the friends I do not like as much as you say.

Verse 2
     D   D
I don't want to do things inde - pendently
       D   D
But I can't make you stay.
G   A   G   D   D   D   D
That's what all the friends I do not like as much as you say.

Chorus 1
          D   D
But if you wanna come back it's alright, it's alright,
G   A
It's alright if you wanna come back.
         D   D
Do you wanna come back? It's alright, it's alright,
G   A   (D)
It's alright if you wanna come back to me.

Link | D | D | D | D |

Verse 3
Well I don't want to see you with another guy
But the fact is that I may.
That's what all the friends I do not like as much as you say.

Verse 4
Well give it just another couple months or so,
Then you'll be ok.
That's what all the friends I do not like as much as you say.

Bridge
       D   D   G   G   A   G   D   D
A - lone,   all a - lone,   I,   I am on my own.
       D   D   G   G   A   G   D   D
A - lone,   all a - lone,   I,   I am on my own.

Chorus 2   As Chorus 1

Solo   ‖: D | D | G | A   :‖

Chorus 3   As Chorus 1 *(Repeat)*

Outro | D | D | D | D |

© COPYRIGHT 2011 GLOBAL TALENT PUBLISHING/UNIVERSAL MUSIC PUBLISHING LIMITED.
ALL RIGHTS RESERVED. INTERNATIONAL COPYRIGHT SECURED.

justinguitar.com

Stage 1
Stage 2
Stage 3
Stage 4
Stage 5
Stage 6
Stage 7
Stage 8
Stage 9
Bonus

 Introduction

This modern classic from The Vaccines is a great, high energy song and ideal for beginners.

Intro to Verse

The first four bars of the intro feature the bass and lead guitar playing high octaves on the note D. The rhythm starts on a D chord, with just one strum every two bars, then moves to two strums per bar (on beats 1 and 3) and then eventually strums on every beat—a great example of a 'build'.

Once the verse starts you'll be playing more sparsely: just one strum on the D chord, letting it ring out for four whole bars. Then just one strum per chord change on the G, A, G, A and back to D. The same applies in Verse 2, although there is an extra strum on the D for the last two bars before the chorus. You should be able to hear these strums pretty clearly and it's good practice to listen closely to the guitar part that you're recreating.

Chorus and Solo

In the chorus we want to pick up the energy—on the recording you'll hear constant eighth-note down-strums (eight down-strums per bar), which will feel very fast after the sparse verses and will give a massive boost to the song! The solo is very achievable for a beginner, so I've written it out in TAB below, but try working it out by ear first.

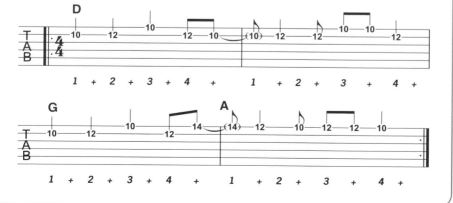

Jolene

Words and Music by Dolly Parton

Capo Fret **4**

Stage 1
Stage 2
Stage 3
Stage 4
Stage 5
Stage 6
Stage 7
Stage 8
Stage 9
Bonus

♩=112

Intro

$\frac{2}{2}$ ‖: Am | Am | Am | Am :‖

Chorus 1

| Am | C | G | Am | Am |

Jo - lene, Jol - ene, Jol - ene, Jo - lene

| G | | G | Am Am Am Am |

I'm begging of you please don't take my man.

| Am | C | G | Am | Am |

Jo - lene, Jo - lene, Jo - lene, Jo - lene

| G | | G | Am Am Am Am |

Please don't take him just because you can.

Verse 1

Am   C

Your beauty is be - yond compare,

G   Am

With flaming locks of auburn hair,

G   G   Am Am Am Am

With iv'ry skin and eyes of em'rald green.

Am   C

Your smile is like a breath of spring,

G   Am

Your voice is soft like summer rain,

G   G   Am Am Am Am

And I cannot com - pete with you, Jolene.

Verse 2

He talks about you in his sleep
And there's nothing I can do to keep
From crying when he calls your name, Jolene.
And I can eas'ly understand
How you could eas'ly take my man
But you don't know what he means to me, Jolene.

Chorus 2

As Chorus 1

Verse 3

You could have your choice of men,
But I could never love again,
He's the only one for me, Jolene.
I had to have this talk with you,
My happiness depends on you
And whatever you decide to do, Jolene.

Chorus 3

Jolene, Jolene, Jolene, Jolene
I'm begging of you please don't take my man.
Jolene, Jolene, Jolene, Jolene
Please don't take him even though you can.

Am Am Am Am

Jolene,   Jolene.

Outro

‖: Am | Am | Am | Am :‖ *Repeat to fade*

© 1973 VELVET APPLE MUSIC- USED BY PERMISSION OF CARLIN MUSIC CORP., LONDON, NW1 8BD FOR THE WORLD (EXCLUDING , SCANDINAVIA, AUSTRALIA AND NEW ZEALAND, JAPAN, SOUTH AFRICA, CANADA AND THE UNITED STATES OF AMERICA). ALL RIGHTS RESERVED. INTERNATIONAL COPYRIGHT SECURED.

Stage 1
Stage 2
Stage 3
Stage 4
Stage 5
Stage 6
Stage 7
Stage 8
Stage 9
Bonus

Introduction

This incredible song, recorded by Dolly Parton in 1973, includes some sublime and complex acoustic guitar parts, although we're going to simplify it for now.

Time signature

The song is in 2/2 time, which is difficult to explain without entering into a full-blown music theory lesson, but there are essentially just two strong beats in the groove, so you'll count two beats per bar, and remember that the chords are displayed for each bar they are played— so during the intro, where Am is written four times, there will be eight beats. Not too difficult, right?

I recommend starting with just two down-strums in each bar—keep it really simple and try to play along with the recording and get used to the song structure. Then try the pattern below—to keep things simple I've written the bar in 4/4 time, but this now means that each beat is twice as fast (around 220bpm), so it'll be pretty quick!

Intro riff

For more advanced players I've also included TAB for the main guitar riff as it is repeated frequently throughout the song. If you're a beginner you should come back to this riff later, as it isn't easy at all!

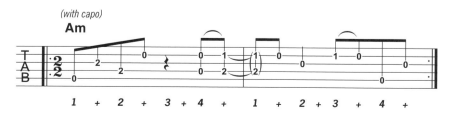

Last Kiss

Words & Music by Wayne Cochran

♩=114

Chorus 1

G .... Em
Oh where, oh where, can my   baby be?
C .... D
  The Lord took her a - way from me.
G .... Em
  She's gone to heaven so I've got to be good,
       C .... D .... G ..... N.C.
So I can see my baby when I leave this world.

Verse 1

       G .... Em
We were out on a date in my daddy's car,
  C .... D
  We hadn't driven very far.
G .... Em
There in the road straight ahead,
  C .... D
A car was stalled, the engine was dead.

Verse 2

G .... Em
I couldn't stop, so I swerved to the right,
    C .... D
I'll never forget the sound that night.
      G .... Em
The screaming tyres, the busting glass,
      C .... D ..... G .... N.C.
The painful scream that I heard last.

Chorus 2   As Chorus 1

Verse 3

When I woke up, the rain was pouring down,
There were people standing all around.
Something warm flowing through my eyes,
But somehow I found my baby that night.

Verse 4

I lifted her head, she looked at me and said,
'Hold me darling just a little while.'
I held her close, I kissed her our last kiss,
I found the love that I knew I had missed.

Verse 5

      G .... Em
Well now she's gone even though I hold her tight,
  C .... D ..... G .... N.C
I lost my love, my life that night.

Chorus 4   As Chorus 1

Outro   ‖: G | Em | C | D   :‖ *(Play x4)*

G

© COPYRIGHT 1961 BOBLO PUBLISHING COMPANY.
LARK MUSIC LIMITED.
ALL RIGHTS RESERVED. INTERNATIONAL COPYRIGHT SECURED.

Stage 1
Stage 2
Stage 3
Stage 4
Stage 5
Stage 6
Stage 7
Stage 8
Stage 9
Bonus

Stage 1
Stage 2
Stage 3
Stage 4
Stage 5
Stage 6
Stage 7
Stage 8
Stage 9
Bonus

 # Introduction

This 1960s song, since popularised by Pearl Jam (whose version we're looking at) is a lovely one to play along with—the chords are simple, and there's a satisfying 'feel' which I'm sure many of you will enjoy, even if the subject matter is a bit intense!

Strumming

I'm hoping you will be familiar with these basic open chords—just watch out (or listen out!) for the stops in the music, shown in the music as N.C (No Chord).

The strumming is pretty consistent throughout and it's our 'Old Faithful' pattern that serves us all so well.

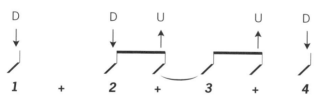

 # Intermediate tricks

More advanced players might like to experiment with picking individual notes out of the chords (I call it 'Picked Fingerstyle', and feature it in my *Intermediate Method*, lesson IM-156) and especially if you get a chance to jam with another guitar player then weaving the basic strumming with more intricate lines and (eventually) fancy barre chord grips make a super cool blend. Check out Pearl Jam's recording for inspiration!

Ooh La La

Words & Music by Ronnie Lane & Ron Wood

Stage 1
Stage 2
Stage 3
Stage 4
Stage 5
Stage 6
Stage 7
Stage 8
Stage 9
Bonus

Capo Fret **7**

♩=148

(Play x5)

Intro

‖: G | G | Am7 | Am7 :‖

Verse 1

G   G   Am7   Am7
Poor old Granddad, I laughed at all his words
   G   G   Am7   Am7
I thought he was a bitter man, he spoke of women's ways.
   G   G   Am7   Am7
They'll trap you, then they use you, be - fore you even know.
   G   G   Am7   Am7
For love is blind and you're far too kind, don't ever let it show.

Chorus 1

G   G   Am7
I wish that I knew what I know now
Am7
When I was younger.
   G   G   Am7
I wish that I knew what I know now
     Am7
When I was stronger.

Am7

×O   O   O

Verse 2

The Can Can's such a pretty show, they'll steal your heart away.
But backstage, back on earth again, the dressing rooms are grey.
They come on strong and it ain't too long
Before they make you feel a man.
But love is blind and you soon will find
You're just a boy again.

Instr

‖: G | C | G | C :‖
| G | C | |
| G | G | Am7 | C |

Verse 3

When you want her lips, you get a cheek,
Makes you wonder where you are.
If you want some more and she's fast asleep,
Then she's twinkling with the stars.
Poor young grandson, there's nothing I can say,
You'll have to learn, just like me,
And that's the hardest way, ooh la la.
Ooh la la la la yeah.

Instr.

| G | G | Am7 | Am7 |

Chorus 2

As Chorus 1

Outro

‖: G | G | Am7 | Am7 :‖ *Repeat to fade*

© COPYRIGHT 1973 WARNER/CHAPPELL MUSIC LIMITED.
ALL RIGHTS RESERVED. INTERNATIONAL COPYRIGHT SECURED.

64

Introduction

In this classic Faces song you are going to get right up the dusty end of the guitar—your capo will be up at the 7th fret.

Chords & strumming

Most of the song is just two chords with a few detours to add a third chord—and that's it! The Am7 chord might not be immediately familiar, but it's the same as a regular Am—just lift off finger 3.

The main strumming pattern is easy as well—simple eighth-note up-and-down-strums. The big deal here is adding a strong backbeat on beats 2 and 4, so really accent those strums to make it groove. Try to make it feel good as you play, so it feels upbeat and danceable!

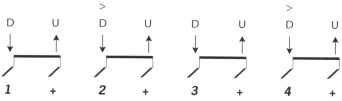

Riff

There is a nice riff on the recording, played by an overdubbed guitar with no capo. You can play this song without a capo using D and Em open chords (and G instead of the occasional C chord), and combining the high capo chords with lower open chords. Try this riff (below), remembering to keep your strumming hand moving all the time.

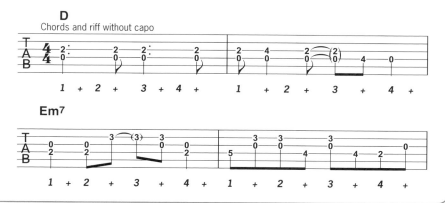

Stage 1
Stage 2
Stage 3
Stage 4
Stage 5
Stage 6
Stage 7
Stage 8
Stage 9
Bonus

Stage 1
Stage 2
Stage 3
Stage 4
Stage 5
Stage 6
Stage 7
Stage 8
Stage 9
Bonus

Radioactive

Words & Music by Alexander Grant, Benjamin McKee,
Daniel Sermon, Daniel Reynolds & Joshua Mosser

Capo Fret 2

♩=138

Intro

(Play x3)

‖: **Am**　　　　| **C**　　　　| **G**　　　　　| **G**　　　　:‖
　Whoa,　　　　oh,　　　　oh.

(G)　　**(G)**　　**(G)**　　**(G)**
Whoa.

Verse 1

Am　　　　　**C**　　　　　**G**
　I'm waking up to ash and dust,
　　　　　　　　D　　　　　**Am**
I wipe my brow and I sweat my rust.
　　　　　　C　　　　　**G**　　**(D)**
I'm breathing in the chemi - cals.

Pre-chorus 1

Am　　　　　**C**　　　　**G**　　　　　**D**　　　　　　　**Am**
　I'm breaking in, shaping up, then checking out on the prison bus.
　　　　　C　　　　**G**　　　　**D**
This is it, the apoca - lypse, whoa.

Chorus 1

　　　　　　Am　　　**C**
I'm waking up, I feel it in my bones,
　　G　　　　　　**D**
E - nough to make my systems blow.
Am　　　　　　　　　　**C**
Welcome to the new age,　to the new age,
G　　　　　　　　　**D**
Welcome to the new age,　to the new age.
Am　　　　　　　　**C**
　Whoa, oh, oh, oh, oh,　whoa, oh, oh, oh,
　G　　　　　**D**
I'm　radioactive,　radioactive.
Am　　　　　　　　**C**
　Whoa, oh, oh, oh, oh,　whoa, oh, oh, oh,
　G　　　　　**(D)**
I'm　radioactive,　radioactive.

Verse 2

I raise my flags, don my clothes
It's a revolution, I suppose.
We'll paint it red to fit right in, whoa.

Pre-chorus 2　As Pre-chorus 1

Chorus 2　As Chorus 1

Bridge

Am　　　**C**　　**G**　　　**D**
All systems go, the sun hasn't died,
Am　　　**C**　　**G**　　　　**D**
Deep in my bones, straight from in - side.

Chorus 3　As Chorus 1

© COPYRIGHT 2012 SONGS OF UNIVERSAL INC/IMAGINE DRAGONS PUBLISHING/JMOSSER MUSIC.
UNIVERSAL/MCA MUSIC LIMITED/BLUE WATER MUSIC UK.
ALL RIGHTS RESERVED. INTERNATIONAL COPYRIGHT SECURED.

Introduction

This song was the breakthrough single for the band Imagine Dragons.

Experimenting

This massive pop hit is an unlikely customer for our *Beginner's Songbook*, but using a capo on fret 2 you can play it using basic open chords. It's a great idea to reinterpret familiar songs, especially as in this case there is no 'set' guitar part in the song—the emphasis is on synth and drums. This means that you can experiment and find your own version (check out the Travis version of 'Hit Me Baby One More Time' for a great example of re-inventing a pop song).

Strumming

So which strumming pattern should you use? Well, you can experiment with that too. A good starting point would be something like the pattern shown below, but I think you should try picking out individual notes too, and even fingerstyle (lesson BC–184 on my website). Don't be shy—get into the experimenting vibe and see what you come up with!

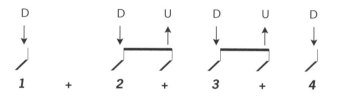

Stage 1
Stage 2
Stage 3
Stage 4
Stage 5
Stage 6
Stage 7
Stage 8
Stage 9
Bonus

Stage 1
Stage 2
Stage 3
Stage 4
Stage 5
Stage 6
Stage 7
Stage 8
Stage 9
Bonus

Songbird

Words & Music by Liam Gallagher

♩=135

Intro

| G | G | |

Verse 1

G   G   G
   Talking to the songbird yester - day
      | G   G/F♯ | Em⁷
Flew me to a place not far a - way.
         Em⁷   Em⁷
She's a little pilot in my mind,
              | Em⁷ G/F♯ | (G)
Singing songs of love to pass the time.

Chorus 1

G   G   G
   Gonna write a song so she can see,
      | G   G/F♯ | Em⁷
Give her all the love she gives to me.
         Em⁷   Em⁷
Talk of better days that have yet to come
         | Em⁷ G/F♯ | G
Never felt this love from any - one.
G   G
   She's not any - one,
| G   G/F♯ | Em⁷
   She's not any - one.
Em⁷   Em⁷ | Em⁷ G/F♯ |
   She's not anyone.

Verse 2

A man can never dream these kind of things
Especially when she came and spread her wings.
Whispered in my ear the things I'd like
Then she flew away into the night.

Chorus 2

Gonna write a song so she can see,
Give her all the love she gives to me.
Talk of better days that have yet to come
Never felt this love from anyone.
She's not anyone, she's not anyone.
She's not anyone.

Instr.

| G | G | G | G   G/F♯ |

| Em⁷ | Em⁷ | Em⁷ | Em⁷   G/F♯ |

| G | G | G | G   G/F♯ |

| Em⁷ | Em⁷ | Em⁷ | Em⁷   G/F♯ | G |

© COPYRIGHT 2002 UNIVERSAL MUSIC PUBLISHING LIMITED. ALL RIGHTS IN GERMANY
ADMINISTERED BY UNIVERSAL MUSIC PUBL. GMBH.
ALL RIGHTS RESERVED. INTERNATIONAL COPYRIGHT SECURED.

Introduction

This is a great acoustic song by Oasis—it's also a good exercise for practising how to sing and play the guitar together.

Extensions and link chords

This is essentially a three-chord song, although the chord grips are slightly different to what you're used to. It'll be easiest to use the three chord grips below, which include the 'big' G chord, and an Em7. The scary-looking G/F♯ links from the G to the Em7 (and then back again); you'll start with the 'big G' chord, using all four fingers, and then simply move finger 1 over to the 2nd fret of string 6 to get the F♯ note.

The Em7 just requires rearranging fingers 1 and 2. The chord can be played as Em, but you'll find the grip below easier, as it means you won't have to move fingers 3 and 4 for the whole song!

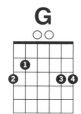

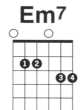

Strumming

There are two patterns you need for this song: one regular pattern and one for when there are two chords in a bar. The 'B' means that you should play a down-strum but aim for the thicker string ('B' for 'Bass'); the rest of the time you should aim for the thinner strings. When there are two chords in a bar (the link chords), play the bass again on beat 3 so that you can hear the transition clearly.

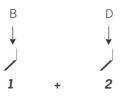

Stage 1
Stage 2
Stage 3
Stage 4
Stage 5
Stage 6
Stage 7
Stage 8
Stage 9
Bonus

Stand By Me

Words & Music by Ben E. King, Jerry Leiber & Mike Stoller

Capo Fret 2

♩=120

Intro

| G | G | Em | Em |
| C | D | G | G |

Verse 1

          G   **G**
When the night has come

Em   **Em**
   And the land is dark

            C   **D**   **G**   **G**
And the moon is the only light we'll see

          G   **G**
No, I won't be a - fraid

        Em   **Em**
Oh, I won't be a - fraid

          C   **D**   **G**
Just as long as you stand, stand by me.

   G
So darling, darling

Chorus 1

G   **G**
Stand by me

    Em   **Em**
Oh, stand by me

    C   **D**   **G**   **G**
Oh, stand,   stand by me,   stand by me.

Verse 2

If the sky that we look upon
Should tumble and fall
Or the mountain should crumble to the sea
I won't cry, I won't cry
No, I won't shed a tear
Just as long as you stand, stand by me.
And darling, darling...

Chorus 2   As Chorus 1

Instrumental

‖: G | G | Em | Em |
| C | D | G | G :‖

2° And darling, darling

Chorus 3   As Chorus 1 *(Repeat to fade)*

© COPYRIGHT 1961 SONY/ATV TUNES LLC, USA.
ADMINISTERED BY HAL LEONARD.
ALL RIGHTS RESERVED. INTERNATIONAL COPYRIGHT SECURED.

Stage 1
Stage 2
Stage 3
Stage 4
Stage 5
Stage 6
Stage 7
Stage 8
Stage 9
Bonus

70

justinguitar.com

Stage 1
Stage 2
Stage 3
Stage 4
Stage 5
Stage 6
Stage 7
Stage 8
Stage 9
Bonus

 # Introduction

This song, recorded by Ben E. King, is an all-time classic and a very popular beginner's song, partly because it's the same eight-bar sequence all the way through. There have been many different interpretations of the song, from fingerstyle to reggae versions, and it's a fun song to experiment with.

Backbeat

The 'backbeat' is the snare drum hit on beats 2 and 4, which you'll hear in countless songs (although there's no snare drum in the original recording, just a very distinctive guiro scrape on beat 2). On the guitar we can create a backbeat by hitting the guitar strings without the outer palm of our strumming hand. You'll play a down-strum on beat 1 and then instead of strumming on beat 2, you'll hit the strings with the outside part of your strumming hand—you want the strings to hit the frets, making a 'metal on metal', percussive sound. This will likely take some practice and you should experiment with where and how hard you should hit—but be aware that it's the thicker strings that will give the loudest sound.

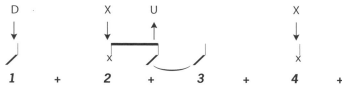

Playing the off beats

Once you have progressed through Stage 4, I recommend that you revisit this song and play only the off beats (the '+'s between the numbers) to give it a laid back reggae feel. It's a great skill to be able play a song in more than one style.

It feels a little strange because you count 1, then do the strum, count 2 then the strum etc., so it will take a little getting used to. You can use either down- or up-strums between the beats in this song; up-strums are probably a little easier though.

Downtown Train

Words & Music by Tom Waits

Stage 1
Stage 2
Stage 3
Stage 4
Stage 5
Stage 6
Stage 7
Stage 8
Stage 9
Bonus

♩=114

Intro

```
| D      | G  A | D      | G  A      |
```

Verse 1

```
 D              G      A      D
   Outside an - other yel - low moon,
                G          A              D
Has punched a hole in the night-time, yes.
 G                              A          D
I climb through the win - dow and down to the street,
   G          A        |
I'm shining like a new dime.
G              A         G          A
   The downtown trains are full   with all those Brooklyn girls,
G                  A
   They try so hard to break out of their little worlds.
```

Verse 2

Well, you wave your hand and they scatter like crows,
They have nothing that will ever capture your heart.
They're just thorns without the rose,
Be careful of them in the dark.
Oh, if I was the one you chose to be your only one,
Oh yeah, can't you hear me now, can't you hear me now?

Chorus 1

```
 D              G   D            G
   Will I see you to - night  on a downtown train?
 D     G                  Em  A              (D)
   Every night it's just the same,    you leave me lonely now.
```

Verse 3

I know your window and I know it's late,
I know your stairs and your doorway.
I walk down your street and past your gate,
I stand by the light at the four-way.
You watch them as they fall,
Oh baby, they all have heart attacks,
They stay at the carnival, but they'll never win you back.

Chorus 2
(double chorus)

Will I see you tonight on a downtown train?
Where every night, every night it's just the same, oh baby.
Will I see you tonight on a downtown train?
All of my dreams they fall like rain,
Oh baby on a downtown train.

Guitar solo

```
| D  A | D  A | D  G | A    |
| D  A | D  A | D  G | A    | A    |
```

Chorus 3

Will I see you tonight on a downtown train?
Where every night, every night it's just the same, oh baby.
Will I see you tonight on a downtown train?
All of my dreams just fall like rain,
All on a downtown train

© COPYRIGHT 1985 JALMA MUSIC
UNIVERSAL MUSIC PUBLISHING MGB LIMITED.
ALL RIGHTS RESERVED. INTERNATIONAL COPYRIGHT SECURED.

```
        D  ‖: G       A        |D    :‖ (x4)
      (...train)  All on a downtown train
Outro      | (D)      | G  A | D       | G  A |
           | D        | G  A | D       |
```

Stage 1

Stage 2

Stage 3

Stage 4

Stage 5

Stage 6

Stage 7

Stage 8

Stage 9

Bonus

 # Introduction

My favourite songwriter Tom Waits works wonders with simple chord progressions and this song can be played using open chords, or power chords (see Stages 7 and 8) if you prefer. Both will sound great! There are also some cool lead lines that you might like to work out.

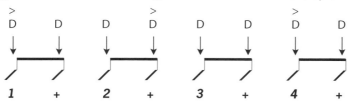# Chords and strumming

You'll be playing 'chugging eighth-notes', meaning that you'll play eight down-strums per bar, using your palm mute (BC-192) to deaden the strings. Once you have the basic 'chug' down, add accents as shown in the rhythm pattern below.

If you play power chords throughout, you'll only need D (root on string 5—there's more info on this in Stage 8) and G and A (both root on string 6) power chords. For the Em, just play the thickest three strings, which will effectively be a power chord too. You'll only be playing the thick strings—be careful to mute string 6 on the D chord with the tip of finger 1.

```
    >                   >                   >
    D    D     D    D     D    D     D    D
    ↓    ↓     ↓    ↓     ↓    ↓     ↓    ↓
    /    /     /    /     /    /     /    /
    1    +     2    +     3    +     4    +
```

Optional chords

The last G and A chords in the verse are actually played as slash chords G/B and A/C♯ which just mean they have a different bass note—I've supplied the relevant chord boxes, but they're not essential to the arrangement.

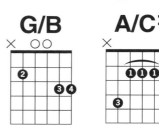

G/B   **A/C♯**

73

Stage 1
Stage 2
Stage 3
Stage 4
Stage 5
Stage 6
Stage 7
Stage 8
Stage 9
Bonus

STAGE 4 BC-141—BC-149

 ## Introduction

Stage 4 introduces some more chords—7th chords, Fmaj7 and a new way to play A—and some variations on strumming patterns. Lots of fun! Remember to add the new strumming patterns to songs you are already confident with, while with the new songs, you should be focusing on the chord changes. Make sure you check out the Stage 4 One-Minute Changes (BC-144) for these new chords because practising changing between them the right way can make a huge difference to how quickly you get them under your fingers. Hopefully you are feeling a bit more confident with your rhythm playing now. Start using these new patterns as soon as you can, remembering to make sure that you are not stopping each time you change chord. In Stage 4 you learn to 'force the changes', which is a really important skill to develop. It will help your songs flow and sound effortless, so make sure you check it out and apply it!

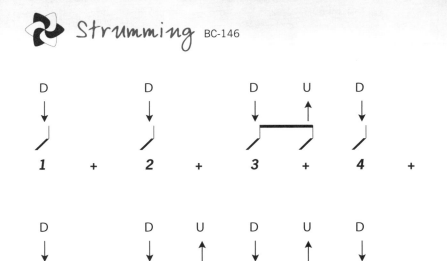

 Stage 4 Chords

G7

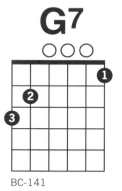

BC-141

C7

BC-141

B7

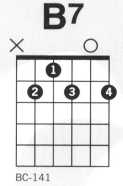

BC-141

Fmaj7

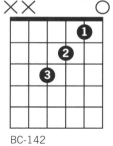

BC-142

A

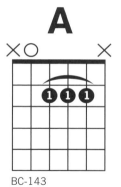

BC-143

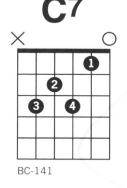

 Stage 4: Your notes

Stage 1
Stage 2
Stage 3
Stage 4
Stage 5
Stage 6
Stage 7
Stage 8
Stage 9
Bonus

Stage 1
Stage 2
Stage 3
Stage 4
Stage 5
Stage 6
Stage 7
Stage 8
Stage 9
Bonus

Closing Time

Words & Music by Dan Wilson

♩=186

Intro ‖: G | D | Am | C :‖ *(Play x3)*

Verse 1

G   D Am   C
Closing time, open all the doors and
G   D   Am C
Let you out into the world.
G   D Am   C
Closing time, turn all of the lights on over
G   D   Am C
Every boy and every girl.

Verse 2

Closing time, one last call for alcohol,
So finish your whiskey or beer.
Closing time, you don't have to go home,
But you can't stay here.

Chorus 1

G   D   Am   C
I know who I want to take me home,
G   D   Am   C
I know who I want to take me home,
G   D   Am   C
I know who I want to take me home,
     G   D Am C
Take me home.

Verse 3

Closing time, time for you to go out to the places you will be from.
Closing time, this room won't be open till your
Brothers or your sisters come.

Verse 4

So gather up your jackets, move it to the exits,
I hope you have found a friend.
Closing time, every new beginning comes from
Some other beginning's end, yeah.

Chorus 2 As Chorus

Instr. 1
Optional synth instrumental

‖: B♭5 | A♭5 | E♭5 | C5 :‖ *(Play x3)*
| G | D | Am | C |

Instr. 2 ‖: G | D | Am | C :‖ *(Play x4)*

Verse 3

Closing time, time for you to go out to the
Places you will be from.

Chorus 3 As Chorus 1 *(Play x2)*

Instr. 3 ‖: G | D | Am | C :‖ *(Play x3)*

Outro verse Closing time, every new beginning comes from
Some other beginning's end.

© COPYRIGHT 1998 WB MUSIC CORPORATION.
WARNER/CHAPPELL NORTH AMERICA LIMITED.
ALL RIGHTS RESERVED. INTERNATIONAL COPYRIGHT SECURED.

Introduction

This hit for Semisonic is a nice easy song for beginners. It's the same four chords throughout, except for a synth instrumental which you'll need power chords for, although most guitarists leave that section out. I've written the tempo as 186bpm, to compensate for the 'half-time' feel of the strumming.

Verse strumming

The strumming isn't entirely consistent but below is the two-bar pattern played at the start—this will work throughout the song, so feel free to do that or just use it as a starting point and make up your own variations as you go along, as per the original recording.

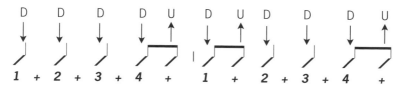

Chorus strumming

The chorus adds some more complexity, using some muted hits, shown below with an X. Strum down on the numbered beats and up on the ands (+). When you see an 'X' shown, make sure your fretting hand is resting lightly on the strings, rather than pressing down on the chords.

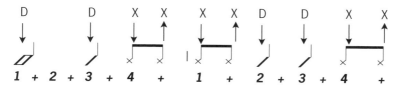

The original version is played using barre chords which makes doing the muted hits a lot more natural as they tend to happen automatically as you change between barre chords.

If you do decide to use barre chords, you can keep the sixth string under your finger barre when you play a root 5 grip—you can hear this clearly in the recording, and whether it was intentional or not, it sounds great!

Stage 1
Stage 2
Stage 3
Stage 4
Stage 5
Stage 6
Stage 7
Stage 8
Stage 9
Bonus

Stage 1
Stage 2
Stage 3
Stage 4
Stage 5
Stage 6
Stage 7
Stage 8
Stage 9
Bonus

3 A.M.

Words & Music by John Stanley, Robert Thomas,
Brian Yale & John Leslie Goff

Capo Fret **1**

♩=108

Intro

let ring...   *let ring...*

| G C(add9) (C(add9)) | G C(add9) (C(add9)) |

‖: G C(add9) | G C(add9) | G C(add9) | G C(add9) :‖

Verse 1

D   C(add9)
   She said it's cold outside
              |G   C(add9)|G C(add9) |
And she hands me my raincoat,

D   C(add9) |G   C(add9)|G C(add9) |
   She's always worried about things like that.

D   C(add9)
   She said it's all gonna end
              |G   C(add9)|G C(add9) |
And it might as well be my fault,
    |D   C(add9)
And she only sleeps when it's raining,
      D   C(add9)
And she screams and her voice is strained.

G

Cadd9

Chorus 1

        |G   D|C(add9)
And she says baby,
    |D |G   D|C(add9)
It's 3a.m. I must be lonely.
      D |G   D|C(add9)
Well, she says baby,
      D |Em   D
Well, I can't help but be scared of it all some - times,
  |C(add9)
The rain is gonna wash away, I believe it.

Link 1

| G C(add9) | G C(add9) | G C(add9) | G C(add9) |

Verse 2

She's got a little bit of something, God it's better than nothing.
And in her colour portrait world, She believes that she's got it all.
She swears the moon don't hang Quite as high as it used to,
And she only sleeps when it's raining,
And she screams and her voice is strained.

Chorus 2

As Chorus 1

Link 3

| C(add9) | C(add9) | C(add9) | C(add9) |

| G C(add9) | G C(add9) | G C(add9) | G C(add9) |

Verse 3

She believes that life is made up of all that you're used to,
And the clock on the wall has been stuck at three for days and days.
She thinks that happiness is a mat that sits on her doorway,

    D   C(add9) C(add9)
But outside it's stopped raining.

© COPYRIGHT 1996 BIDNIS INCORPORATED/EMI BLACKWOOD MUSIC INCORPORATED/U RULE MUSIC/TECKLAH MUSIC.
COPYRIGHT CONTROL/IQ MUSIC LIMITED/EMI MUSIC PUBLISHING LIMITED.
ALL RIGHTS RESERVED. INTERNATIONAL COPYRIGHT SECURED.

| Chorus 3 | As Chorus 1 |

Chorus 3   As Chorus 1

Chorus 4   Well, it's 3a.m. I must be lonely, well, heaven she says baby,
Well, I can't help but be scared of it all sometimes.

Introduction

This pop ballad was written and recorded by Matchbox 20.

Layers and strumming

This song combined an acoustic guitar strumming, and a clean electric
guitar playing picked-out notes and ornaments. We're going to focus on
the acoustic guitar part. There's a new chord: Cadd9, which you can
simplify to C if you want, although it's not hard.

I've summarised the acoustic guitar part into two patterns: one for the
verse, and once for the chorus. I have written these strumming patterns
out at half speed, making them easier to learn, although you will have to
adjust the speed when you apply them to the song itself.

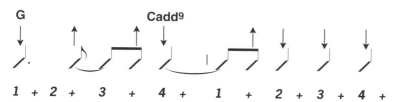

During the intro, you should only play the first four strums of the **verse**
pattern (shown above) and then let the fourth strum (the Cadd9) ring out.
Once the drums enter, you should play the full verse strumming pattern,
although be aware that once you reach the verse, the D and Cadd9
chords are played just once on beat 1 of each bar and left to ring out.

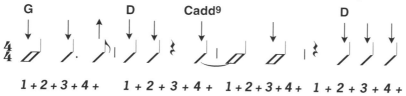

The **chorus** introduces another pattern (above), which includes quite a
few heavy accents. The guide pattern above highlights these accents,
however you should find that you naturally play more strums than those
shown, so be flexible when playing this pattern—start by tackling the
accents, and then fill in some of the beats either side of them.

Stage 1
Stage 2
Stage 3
Stage 4
Stage 5
Stage 6
Stage 7
Stage 8
Stage 9
Bonus

Girl, You'll Be A Woman Soon

Words & Music by Neil Diamond

Capo Fret **3**

♩=110

Intro

Em A   D   Em   Em
Girl,   you'll be a woman soon.

Verse 1

Em
Love you so much can't count all the ways,

   Em   D   D
I'd die for you girl and all they can say is   he's not your kind.

      Em
They never get tired of putting me down,

   Em   D   D
And I never know when I come around   what I'm gonna find.

         C   C
Don't let them make up your mind.

Chorus 1

(C)   Em A   D   Em
Don't you know girl,   you'll be a woman soon,

Em   A   D   D
Please,   come take my hand.

Em A   D   Em
Girl,   you'll be a woman soon,

Em   A   D   D
Soon   you'll need a man.

Verse 2

I've been misunderstood for all of my life,
But what they're saying, girl, just cuts like a knife; the boy's no good.
Well, I finally found what I've been looking for,
But if they get the chance, they'll end it for sure, sure they would.
Baby, I've done all I could.

Chorus 2

It's up to you girl, you'll be a woman soon...

Instr.

| C | C | B7 | B7 | |
| C | C | B7 | B7 | ‖ |

Chorus 3

Oh girl, you'll be a woman soon....

Em   A   D   D
Soon   you'll need a man.   *Repeat last line to fade*

© COPYRIGHT 1967 TALLYRAND MUSIC INCORPORATED, USA.
UNIVERSAL/MCA MUSIC LIMITED.
ALL RIGHTS RESERVED. INTERNATIONAL COPYRIGHT SECURED.

Stage 1 · Stage 2 · Stage 3 · Stage 4 · Stage 5 · Stage 6 · Stage 7 · Stage 8 · Stage 9 · Bonus

Stage 1
Stage 2
Stage 3
Stage 4
Stage 5
Stage 6
Stage 7
Stage 8
Stage 9
Bonus

 # Introduction

We're looking at the original Neil Diamond recording of this song from 1967. It's one of those songs that feels like it's been around forever and features some tasteful guitar work.

 ## Strumming

Neil Diamond plays this with a capo on fret 3, which simplifies the chords and will allow you to focus on your strumming groove. The opening of the song uses simple spread chords—just play the chord once and let it ring out. When the groove kicks in, the acoustic guitar plays a lovely pattern shown below. There are some variations but you should get the main groove under your fingers first.

On beats 2 and 4 you can mute the chord—do a percussive hit on the strings if you know how, otherwise it's okay to let it ring out. Keep it simple if you're a beginner or try new things if you're finding it easy!

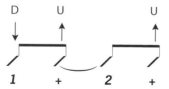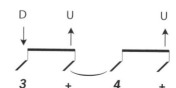

 ## Jam buddy

If you have buddy to jam with, you can try the electric guitar part too—a simple clean sound with a little tremolo on it, strummed each chord change will sound amazing when combined with the acoustic guitar. It's a classic blend!

In the chorus you can change the strum pattern to either 'Old Faithful' (page 19) or for a challenge, replicate what I call 'picked fingerstyle' (covered in the *Intermediate Method*, lesson IM-156), where as you strum, instead of picking all the strings with each movement, you just pick out one or two notes. On the original recording, the song starts with picked fingerstyle and morphs into Old Faithful!

If It Makes You Happy

Words & Music by Sheryl Crow & Jeffrey Trott

♩=96

G
×○○○

Gsus2/4
×○

Intro

‖: G │ Gsus2/4 │ G │ Gsus2/4 :‖

Verse 1

        G   Gsus2/4   G   Gsus2/4
I be - long   a long way from here,
G   Gsus2/4
Put on a poncho, played for mosquitos
         G   C
And drank till I was thirsty a - gain.
             G   Gsus2/4   G   Gsus2/4
We went searching   through thrift store jungles,
            G   Gsus2/4
Found Ge - ronimo's rifle, Marilyn's shampoo,
         G   C
And Benny Goodman's corset and pen.
        C   D   C   D   N.C
Well ok, I made this up, I promised you I'd never give up.

Chorus 1

                   Am   C   G   D
If it makes you happy,   It can't be that bad.
                   Am   C   (G)
If it makes you happy,   then why the hell are you so sad?

Link

│ G │ Gsus2/4 │ G │ Gsus2/4 │

Verse 2

You get down, real low down.
You listen to Coltrane, derail your own train
Well who hasn't been there before?
I come round, around the hard way.
Bring you comics in bed, scrape the mould off the bread
And serve you French toast again.
Well ok, I still get stoned, I'm not the kind of girl you'd take home.

Chorus 2

As Chorus 1

Chorus 3

(G) (G)   Am   C   G   D
      If it makes you happy,   It can't be that bad.
                   Am   C   Em   Em
If it makes you happy,   then why the hell are you so sad?

Interlude

│ Am │ Am │ Em │ Em │

│ C │ C │ G │ Gsus2/4 │ G │ Gsus2/4 │

Verse 3

We've been far, far away from here,
Put on a poncho, played for mosquitos and everywhere in between,
Well ok, we get along, so what if right now everything's wrong?

Chorus 4

As Chorus 1 *(Repeat chorus to fade)*

© COPYRIGHT 1996 TROTTSKY MUSIC/
CHRYSALIS ONE MUSIC PUBLISHING GROUP IRELAND LTD.
CHRYSALIS ONE PUBLISHING UK LIMITED/WIXEN MUSIC UK LTD.
ALL RIGHTS RESERVED. INTERNATIONAL COPYRIGHT SECURED.

Stage 1   Stage 2   Stage 3   Stage 4   Stage 5   Stage 6   Stage 7   Stage 8   Stage 9   Bonus

Stage 1
Stage 2
Stage 3
Stage 4
Stage 5
Stage 6
Stage 7
Stage 8
Stage 9
Bonus

Introduction

This was a big hit for one of pop's most impressive singer-songwriters, Sheryl Crow. It was a single from her eponymous album, released in 1996.

Chords and riff

There's a very laid-back groove here which is fairly straightforward. You'll need to get comfortable with a slightly unusual chord, the Gsus2/4, and changing to it from a version of a G chord which uses only fingers 3 and 4. Just add fingers 1 and 2 (as shown in the chord box) and you'll have a Gsus2/4. Below is the main sequence, as TAB.

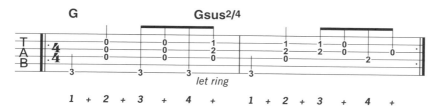

Strumming

You don't have to stick with the riff if you didn't want to. The basic strumming pattern from the record varies throughout but is based on the following two-bar pattern.

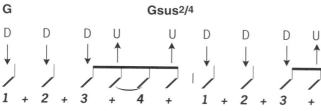

There are a couple of single bars in the verses—keep an ear out for these, as they might throw you off course, and the pattern usually changes to something like this:

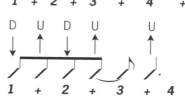

One

Words & Music by U2

♩=90

Verse 1

Am   D Fmaj⁷   G
 Is it getting better, or do you feel the same?

Am   D   Fmaj⁷   G
 Will it make it easier on you, now you got someone to blame?

Chorus 1

    C   Am
You say one love, one life,

Fmaj⁷   C
 When it's one need in the night.

C   Am
 One love, we get to share it,

Fmaj⁷   C
 Leaves you baby if you don't care for it.

Verse 2

Did I disappoint you, or leave a bad taste in your mouth?
You act like you never had love and you want me to go without.

Chorus 2

Well it's too late tonight, to drag the past out into the light.
We're one, but we're not the same.
We get to carry each other, carry each other…one!

Verse 3

Have you come here for forgiveness, have you come to raise the dead
Have you come here to play Jesus to the lepers in your head?

Chorus 3

Did I ask too much, more than a lot?
You gave me nothing, now it's all I got.
We're one, but we're not the same,
Well, we hurt each other, then we do it again.

Middle

    C   Am
You say love is a temple, love a higher law,

   C   Am
Love is a temple, love the higher law.

   C   G
You ask me to enter, but then you make me crawl,

   G   Fmaj⁷
And I can't be holding on to what you got,

Fmaj⁷   C
 When all you got is hurt.

Chorus 4

One love, one blood,
One life, you got to do what you should.
One life, with each other,
Sisters, brothers.
One life, but we're not the same,
We get to carry each other, carry each other.

© COPYRIGHT 1991 BLUE MOUNTAIN MUSIC LIMITED (FOR THE UK)/MOTHER MUSIC (FOR THE REPUBLIC OF IRELAND)/UNIVERSAL INTERNATIONAL MUSIC PUBLISHING B.V. (FOR THE REST OF THE WORLD). ALL RIGHTS RESERVED. INTERNATIONAL COPYRIGHT SECURED.

Introduction

Artistic differences during the recording of U2's seventh studio album, *Achtung Baby*, threatened to split the band apart. 'One' is credited as the breakthrough song that turned those sessions around.

 Dsus2

The D chord in 'One' is played by The Edge as a Dsus2 chord. Although The Edge plays this chord as a barre chord, we can substitute it for a very easy open chord. Sus chords are a big part of U2's sound, and you'll find more information on the chords themselves on page 147.

Dsus2

 Strumming

There are many subtle strums used in this song and some nice little inflections with the fretting hand too. The place to start is with the following pattern, and then build in some extra strums lightly as you get more confident with it. As usual, listen to the original recording and try your best to emulate it. Really this is sixteenth-note strumming, but I've shown it here as two bars of eighth-notes. So you'll have to play both bars of the pattern for each chord. To play at speed you'll also have to double the tempo to 180bpm (from 90bpm).

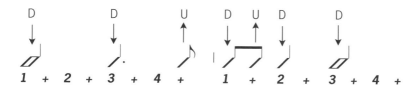

Stage 1
Stage 2
Stage 3
Stage 4
Stage 5
Stage 6
Stage 7
Stage 8
Stage 9
Bonus

Seen It All

Words & Music by Jake Bugg & Iain Archer

Capo Fret **2**

♩=166

Verse 1

Em C G D/F#
 One Friday night I took a pill or maybe two.
Em C G D/F#
 Down at the car park I saw everyone I knew.
  Em C G D/F#
And be - fore the night had started we had planned to crash a party,
  Em C
Just a place that someone knew
  G D/F# (Em)
A local house belonging to a gangster's crew.

D/F#
×○ ×
❶ ❷
    ❸

Link 1

| Em | C | G | D/F# |

Verse 2

And at the door they shone a light into my face,
Have to admit I felt a little out of place.
But I made my way inside past a thousand crazy eyes,
Then a friend took me aside said everyone here has a knife.

Chorus 1

  C C G D
I've seen it all, I've seen it all now.
  C Am
I swear to God I've seen it all
  G D (Em)
Nothing shocks me any more after to - night.

Link 2

| Em | C | G | D/F# |

Verse 3

Those little doves had sent my mind and heart a-beating,
To say I felt weird really doesn't need repeating.
I could sense the mounting tension, the atmosphere of violence
And then they took a guy outside
And someone stabbed him with a knife.

Chorus 2

As Chorus 1

Link 3

‖: Em | C | G | D/F# :‖

Chorus 3

  C C G D
I've seen it all, I've seen it all now,
  C C G D
I've seen it all, I've seen it all now,
  C Am
I swear to God I've seen it all,
  G D Am Am
Nothing shocks me any more after to - night,
  G G Am Am G
I've seen the light but not the kind I would have liked.

© COPYRIGHT 2012 KOBALT MUSIC SERVICES LTD/SOUL KITCHEN MUSIC LIMITED.
KOBALT MUSIC PUBLISHING LIMITED.
ALL RIGHTS RESERVED. INTERNATIONAL COPYRIGHT SECURED.

Introduction

As well as being a cool tune, this track from Jake Bugg is a great song to work on your accents.

 Accents

Listen to the original track and you'll clearly hear Jake getting into a groove by playing even eighth-notes but putting a heavy accent on beats 2 and 4. Remember that you'll achieve the accent by playing harder—but also by playing the other notes a bit softer, and you'll probably need to adopt both approaches to get the accents as pronounced as they are in this song.

 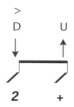 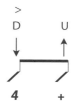

 Chords, chunks and charts

I'd recommend breaking the song into 'chunks' in order to remember the individual progressions: the intro and verses are just Em C G D/F♯ and the chorus is C C G D, C Am G D. The D/F♯ looks daunting but is pretty simple—the trick is to mute string 5 with your index finger, by lightly touching the string.

Learning to simplify songs in your mind can really help you remember them—I make simple little cheat charts for almost every song I learn and I find later I can recall the image of the cheat chart and read it mentally, which I certainly wouldn't be able to do with a full sheet of chords and lyrics. Perhaps the writing it out helps too, but I think there is something vital about looking for the simple, recurring patterns too!

Stage 1
Stage 2
Stage 3
Stage 4
Stage 5
Stage 6
Stage 7
Stage 8
Stage 9
Bonus

Stay With Me

Words & Music by Tom Petty, Jeff Lynne, James Napier,
Sam Smith & William Phillips

♩=85

Stage 1
Stage 2
Stage 3
Stage 4
Stage 5
Stage 6
Stage 7
Stage 8
Stage 9
Bonus

Verse 1

|Am   Fmaj7 |C
  Guess it's true, I'm not good at a one night stand,
|Am   Fmaj7 |C
  But I still need love 'cause I'm just a man.
|Am   Fmaj7 |C
  These nights never seem to go to plan,
|Am7   Gsus4 |C
  I don't want you to leave, will you hold my hand?

Chorus 1

(C) |Am   Fmaj7 |C
Oh, won't you   stay with me?
             |Am Fmaj7 |C
'Cause you're   all I   need.
G |Am   Fmaj7 |C
This ain't love, it's clear to see,
      E7 |Am   Fmaj7 |C
But darling,   stay with me.

Verse 2

Why am I so emotional?
No, it's not a good look, gain some self-control.
And deep down I know this never works,
But you can lay with me so it doesn't hurt.

Chorus 2

As Chorus 1

Instr.

| Am   Fmaj7 | C | Am   Fmaj7 | C |

| Am   Fmaj7 | C | Am   Gsus4 | C |

Chorus 3

As Chorus 1

Chorus 4

As Chorus 1

© COPYRIGHT 2014 STELLAR SONGS LIMITED/NAUGHTY WORDS LIMITED/EMI APRIL MUSIC INC/
GONE GATOR MUSIC/SALLI ISAAK SONGS LIMITED/METHOD PAPERWORK LTD.
UNIVERSAL MUSIC PUBLISHING LIMITED/EMI MUSIC PUBLISHING LIMITED/
SONY/ATV MUSIC PUBLISHING/WIXEN MUSIC UK LTD.
ALL RIGHTS RESERVED. INTERNATIONAL COPYRIGHT SECURED.

Stage 1

Stage 2

Stage 3

Stage 4

Stage 5

Stage 6

Stage 7

Stage 8

Stage 9

Bonus

 Introduction

Sam Smith struck gold with this massive hit song. It's pretty simple but has some interesting rhythm 'pushes', which will require attention.

Pushes

So what is a 'push'? Well, a push is when a chord is moved early, in this case by an eighth-note. In this song the pushes are fairly obvious because you only need to play each chord once and let it ring out, so when you play the chord becomes even more important!

The main sequence is shown below—the push is on the C chord, which is played on '4+' rather than on beat 1 of the next bar. It's been 'pushed' earlier!

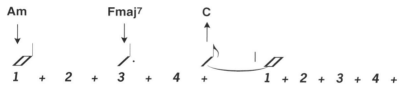

In the chorus we have almost the same rhythmic pattern but some of the bars have an additional chord on beat 4, after the C chord.

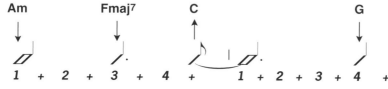

 Gsus4

Note that the Gsus4 chord on the original is an F/G but that's a pretty tricky chord for beginners. You have a few options there—you can just play G, or you could play Gsus4 or F/G depending on your finger dexterity. I'd recommend sticking with the Gsus4 chord, making sure you mute string 1 (with your first finger) and string 6 (with your third finger).

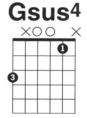

Gsus4

Stage 1
Stage 2
Stage 3
Stage 4
Stage 5
Stage 6
Stage 7
Stage 8
Stage 9
Bonus

Sugar

Words & Music by Adam Levine, Lukasz Gottwald, Joshua Coleman, Mike Posner, Henry Russell Walter & Jacob Hindlin

Capo Fret 1

♩=120

Sequence throughout:

| Fmaj⁷ | Am | Dm | C |

Intro

Play Sequence x1

Verse 1

I'm hurting, baby, I'm broken down,
I need your loving, loving, I need it now.
When I'm without you, I'm something weak,
You got me begging, begging, I'm on my knees.

Pre-chorus 1

I don't wanna be needing your love,
I just wanna be deep in your love,
And it's killing me when you're away, ooh, baby,
'Cause I really don't care where you are,
I just wanna be there where you are,
And I gotta get one little taste.

Chorus 1

Your sugar, yes, please,
Won't you come and put it down on me?
I'm right here, 'cause I need,
Little love, a little sympathy.
Yeah, you show me good loving, make it alright.
Need a little sweetness in my life.
Your sugar, yes, please,
Won't you come and put it down on me?

Verse 2

My broken pieces, you pick them up.
Don't leave me hanging, hanging, come give me some
When I'm without ya, I'm so insecure,
You are the one thing, one thing, I'm living for.

Pre-chorus 2

As Pre-chorus 1

Chorus 2

As Chorus 1

Verse 3

I want that red velvet, I want that sugar sweet.
Don't let nobody touch it, unless that somebody's me.
I gotta be your man, there ain't no other way
'Cause girl you're hotter than a southern California day
I don't wanna play no games, you don't gotta be afraid
Don't give me all that shy ****,
No make-up on, that's my...

Chorus 3

As Chorus 1 *(Play x2)*

Outro

Play Sequence x1

© COPYRIGHT 2014 KASZ MONEY PUBLISHING/SONY/ATV TUNES LLC/EACH NOTE COUNTS/PRESCRIPTION
SONGS/NORTH GREENWAY PRODUCTIONS/KOBALT MUSIC COPYRIGHTS SARL/
CIRKUT BREAKER LLC/SUDGEE 2 MUSIC
SONY/ATV MUSIC PUBLISHING (UK) LIMITED/KOBALT MUSIC PUBLISHING LIMITED
ALL RIGHTS RESERVED. INTERNATIONAL COPYRIGHT SECURED.

Stage 1
Stage 2
Stage 3
Stage 4
Stage 5
Stage 6
Stage 7
Stage 8
Stage 9
Bonus

Introduction

Here's another mega hit from the Maroon 5 crew, and another song with the same chord sequence throughout. They're masters of the 'one chord progression for the whole song' technique!

Starting out

I recommend starting by playing one strum per bar, and playing along with the record. That's fun already! Once you're happy with that, you could try adding in some more strums to capture the feel of the recording. Try the strumming pattern below, keeping the strums tight and short for a 'pop' feel, or let them ring out for a more relaxed feel.

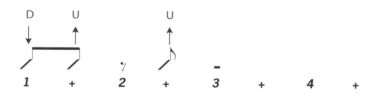

Up for a challenge?

If you're up for a challenge, try using these more advanced chord grips, which are a lot closer to the grips used on the original recording. The Fmaj7 chord is actually a C/F chord, as shown below, and the Am and Dm are 'm7' chords, as shown, while the C chord remains the same.

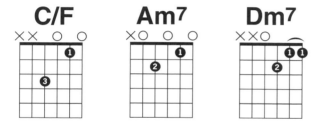

There are loads of covers around of this song and it's a great one to make up your own version of—try different strumming patterns, fingerstyle patterns, different tempos—try it all and see what you like!

Stage 1 Stage 2 Stage 3 Stage 4 Stage 5 Stage 6 Stage 7 Stage 8 Stage 9 Bonus

What I Like About You

Words & Music by Mike Skill, Jimmy Marinos & Wally Palamarchuk

♩=160

riff

Intro ‖: E   A | D (Asus⁴) A | E   A | D   A :‖

Play **riff x4**

Verse 1

riff x2
What I like about you,
You hold me tight,
Tell me I'm the only one,
Wanna come over tonight, yeah.

Asus⁴

Chorus 1

riff x2
Keep on whispering in my ear,
Tell me all the things that I wanna hear,
'Cause it's true (that's what I like)
That's what I like about you (that's what I like).

Verse 2

What I like about you,
You really know how to dance.
When you go up, down, jump around,
Think about true romance, yeah.

Chorus 2

riff x3
Keep on whispering in my ear,
Tell me all the things that I wanna hear,
'Cause it's true (that's what I like about you)
That's what I like about you (that's what I like about you),
That's what I like about you (that's what I like about you),
That's what I like about you (that's what I like about you).

Instrumental | G | D | G | A |

| A | B⁷ | B⁷ | B⁷   N.C. |
                                              Hey!

Solo Play **riff x2**

Verse 3

What I like about you,
You keep me warm at night,
Never wanna let you go,
Know you make me feel all right, yeah.

Chorus 3 As Chorus 2
That's what I like about you... *(x4)*

Play **riff x3**

© COPYRIGHT 1980 EMI APRIL MUSIC INCORPORATED, USA
EMI MUSIC PUBLISHING LTD.
ALL RIGHTS RESERVED. INTERNATIONAL COPYRIGHT SECURED.

Introduction

This hit for The Romantics is a great song for working on your A, D and E chords, and the new way of playing A that we checked out earlier in Stage 4.

Easy strumming

At first, I'd recommend leaving out the Asus4 chord, and just playing two strums per chord, before graduating to this simplified pattern.

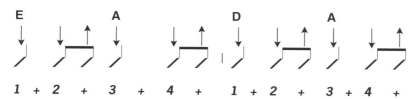

Now for the Asus4—this comes after the D chord, so leave finger 3 where it is on the D (fret 3, string 2) and move finger 1 over to play a mini barre covering strings 4, 3 and 2. Lift off finger 3 to 'reveal' the A chord.

You can carry on with the previous pattern, now adding the Asus4, and that will work well enough. The actual pattern is quite tricky but it's super cool. Just take it slowly and get used to exactly where the chords change.

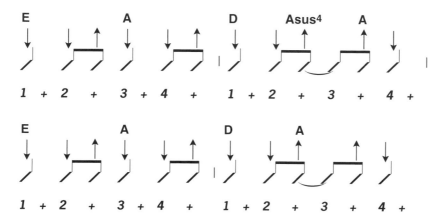

Notice that I've simplified the bridge section, as the original is too tricky for beginners. It's basically the same chords as I've shown but includes an Asus4 (as used in the riff) and uses a B barre chord (rather than the open B7 shown) using a sus 4 shape (adding the little finger on fret 5 string 2).

Budapest

Words & Music by Joel Pott & George Ezra Barnett

Stage 1
Stage 2
Stage 3
Stage 4
Stage 5
Stage 6
Stage 7
Stage 8
Stage 9
Bonus

♩=128

Intro
| G | G | G | G |

Verse 1

G
  My house in Budapest, my,   my hidden treasure chest,   (G)
G   G
  Golden grand piano,   my beautiful Castillo.
C   C   G   G
You, ooh, you, ooh, I'd leave it all.
G   G
  My acres of a land,   I have achieved.
G   G
  It may be hard for you to   stop and believe.
C   C   G   G
But for you, ooh, you, ooh, I'd leave it all.
C   C   G   G
Oh for you, ooh, you, ooh, I'd leave it all.

Chorus 1

D   C   G   G
Give me one good reason why I should never make a change.
D   C   G   G
And baby if you hold me then all of this will go a - way.

Verse 2

My many artefacts, the list goes on,
If you just say the words, I'll, I'll up and run.
Oh, to you, ooh, you, ooh, I'd leave it all.
Oh, to you, ooh, you, ooh, I'd leave it all.

Chorus 2

As Chorus 1 *(Play x2)*

Instrumental
| G | G | G | G |
| C | C | G | G |

Verse 3

My friends and family, they, don't understand,
They fear they'd lose so much if you take my hand.
But, for you, ooh, you, ooh, I'd lose it all.
Oh for you, ooh, you, ooh, I'd lose it all.

Chorus 3

As Chorus 2

Verse 4

My house in Budapest, my, my hidden treasure chest,
Golden grand piano, my beautiful Castillo.
You, ooh, you, ooh, I'd leave it all.
Oh for you, ooh, you, ooh I'd leave it all.

© COPYRIGHT 2013 CHRYSALIS MUSIC LIMITED/BMG RIGHTS MANAGEMENT (UK) LIMITED, A BMG CHRYSALIS COMPANY.
ALL RIGHTS RESERVED. INTERNATIONAL COPYRIGHT SECURED.

Introduction

This track by the incredibly young George Ezra is a great song to strum through, and I'll also show you simple the fingerstyle technique that George uses.

 Capos and tuning

George Ezra plays a baritone guitar for this song—this is tuned a 4th lower than a regular guitar—and on which he places a capo at the 3rd fret. So the accumulative effect is that it sounds like he's tuned a regular guitar down a whole tone. If you want to play along with the recording, that's what you'll need to do (unless you use software, such as *Transcribe!*, to raise the pitch of the recording). The detuned strings would be (from low to high): D,G,C,F,A,D.

 Strumming

I'd recommend starting with the regular four down-strums per bar and getting familiar with the structure and the chord changes, and then perhaps moving on to playing 'Old Faithful', a dependable strumming pattern that I'm sure you'll get to know well!

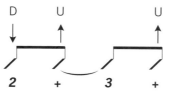

Stage 1
Stage 2
Stage 3
Stage 4
Stage 5
Stage 6
Stage 7
Stage 8
Stage 9
Bonus

continued...

95

Stage 1 Stage 2 Stage 3 **Stage 4** Stage 5 Stage 6 Stage 7 Stage 8 Stage 9 Bonus

❧ Fingerstyle playing

George Ezra plays this song by employing a kind of fingerstyle technique, where the thumb plays the bass note and then fingers 1, 2 and 3 play the notes of the chord all at once. It takes some practice to get the right feel, but it's not very tricky once your muscle memory kicks in. Just remember to take it slowly and get it right before speeding it up.

The intro includes a cool hammer-on (on string 5), where you pluck the open A and then quickly 'hammer' your first finger down on to fret 2. This pattern occurs during the intro, and then later during the breaks between the singing.

I've also written out patterns for the G chord (when there is singing over the top of it), the C and D chords. Be aware that when you're changing from the G or C chords, the penultimate note in the pattern (which I've put in brackets) is played as an open string.

❧ TAB

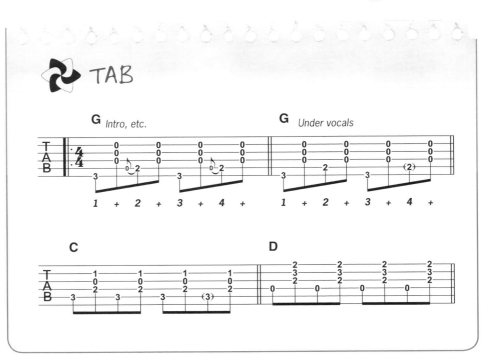

Stage 1

Stage 2

Stage 3

Stage 4

Stage 5

Stage 6

Stage 7

Stage 8

Stage 9

Bonus

Stage 4: Final notes

Are there any songs or techniques that you want to revisit later in the course? Write them down!

STAGE 5 BC-151—BC-159

Introduction

We've now looked at most of the open position 7th chords, which means you can play a blues in several different keys, and for that reason, many of the songs in this stage are blues-based. They should be a lot of fun to play, and as you learn more blues licks and techniques you will be able to apply them to these songs too, but it's best to start by strumming through them to get the groove really solid.

The best way to learn the grooves in blues is to listen to blues musicians performing, either live or most likely on a recording. Blues is an aural tradition—it is passed down to the next generation by people listening—and so you can't learn the blues by reading or through academic study. If you are not familiar with these artists then go and buy a few albums and get the sounds, songs and feel into your head!

As ever, keep going with your One-Minute Changes (BC-154) and also have a look at Air Changes (BC-153).

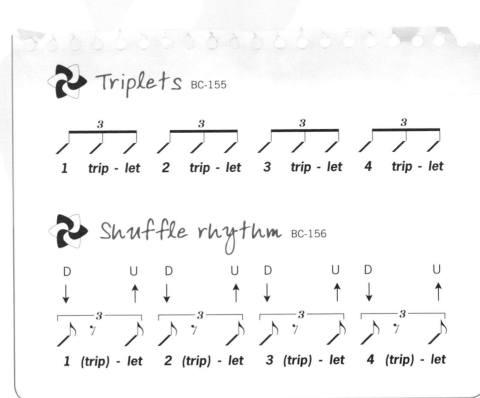

Triplets BC-155

3	3	3	3
1 trip - let	2 trip - let	3 trip - let	4 trip - let

Shuffle rhythm BC-156

D	U	D	U	D	U	D	U

| 1 (trip) - let | 2 (trip) - let | 3 (trip) - let | 4 (trip) - let |

 Stage 5 Chords

A7

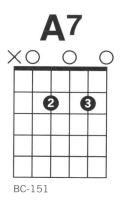

BC-151

D7

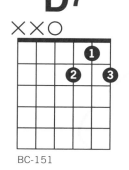

BC-151

E7

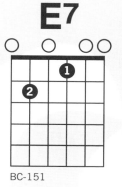

BC-151

 Stage 5: Your notes

Stage 1
Stage 2
Stage 3
Stage 4
Stage 5
Stage 6
Stage 7
Stage 8
Stage 9
Bonus

Blue Suede Shoes

Words & Music by Carl Lee Perkins

Stage 1
Stage 2
Stage 3
Stage 4
Stage 5
Stage 6
Stage 7
Stage 8
Stage 9
Bonus

♩=190

Verse 1

          A7   **A7**
Well it's a-one for the money, two for the show,
A7   **A7**
Three to get ready, now go, cat, go…

Chorus 1

     D7   **D7**   **A7**   **A7**
But don't you step on my blue suede shoes.
           E7   **E7**   **A7**   **A7**
You can do anything but lay off of my blue suede shoes.

Verse 2

             A7   **A7**
Well, you can knock me down, step on my face,
A7   **A7**
Slander my name all over the place,
A7   **A7**
Do anything that you want to do,
     A7   **A7**
But ah-ah honey lay off of them shoes…

Chorus 2

As Chorus 1   *(Let's go, cats!)*

Solo 1

| **A7** | **A7** | **A7** | **A7** | **D7** | **D7** | |
| **A7** | **A7** | **E7** | **E7** | **A7** | **A7** | |

Verse 3

You can burn my house, steal my car,
Drink my liquor from an old fruit jar.
Well do anything that you want to do,
But ah-ah honey lay off of my shoes…

Chorus 3

As Chorus 1   *(Rock it!)*

Solo 2

As Solo 1

Verse 4

Well it's one for the money, two for the show,
Three to get ready, now go, go, go.

Chorus 4

As Chorus 1

Outro

       A7   **A7**
Well it's   blue, blue, blue suede shoes,
A7   **A7**
 Blue, blue, blue suede shoes, yeah!
D7   **D7**
 Blue, blue, blue suede shoes, baby!
A7   **A7**
 Blue, blue, blue suede shoes,
           E7   **E7**   **A7**   **A7**
Well you can do anything but lay off of my blue suede shoes.

© COPYRIGHT 1955, 1956 HI LO MUSIC, INC.
© COPYRIGHT RENEWED 1983, 1984 CARL PERKINS MUSIC, INC.
ADMINISTERED BY WREN MUSIC CO., A DIVISION OF MPL MUSIC PUBLISHING, INC.
ALL RIGHTS RESERVED. INTERNATIONAL COPYRIGHT SECURED. USED BY PERMISSION.

Stage 1
Stage 2
Stage 3
Stage 4
Stage 5
Stage 6
Stage 7
Stage 8
Stage 9
Bonus

 # Introduction

This all-time classic from Elvis Presley has a couple of characteristic tricks which you'll definitely need to know if you're going to play blues or rock 'n' roll music.

 ## Stops

The first trick is the 'stops' during the verses. Start by playing just the first beat of the bar, quickly muting it with the outside of your strumming hand (in Verse 1, you'll play on the lyrics 'One...Two...Three...' Then, add the two 'pick-up' accents before the beat, as shown below. This pattern happens three times, followed by a build into the chorus.

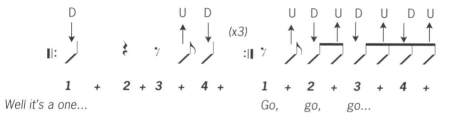

Well it's a one...

 ## Chorus

During the chorus, I recommend you use even eighth-notes and play with loads of energy! You have two options for adding accents (playing some strums a bit louder, marked below by a >). You can either play just the first bar shown below, or you can extend it to the whole two-bar pattern if you want more of a challenge.

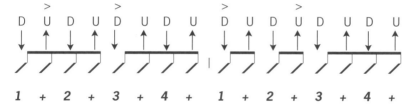

101

Ice Cream Man

Words & Music by John Brim

♩=178

Intro

| E7 | E7 | E7 | E7 | |

Verse 1

E7   A7   E7   E7
Summertime is here babe, need somethin' to keep you cool
    A7   A7   E7   E7
Ah now, summertime is here, need somethin' to keep you cool
B7   A7   E7
Better look out now though, I got somethin' for you,
         | E7   B7 |
Tell ya what it is:

Chorus 1

(B7)   E7   A7   E7   E7
I'm your ice cream man, stop me when I'm passin' by (Oh my, my)
       A7   A7   E7   E7
I'm your ice cream man, stop me when I'm passin' by
    B7   A7 | E7   B7 |
See now all my flavors are guaranteed to satis - fy (Hold on a second)

Chorus 2

   E7   E7   E7   E7
I got puddin' pie, banana, dixie cups,   all flavors and pushups too
    A7   A7   E7   E7
I'm your ice cream man baby, stop me when I'm passin' by
    B7   A7   E7 | E7   B7 |
See now all my flavors are guaranteed to satis - fy (hold on, one more)

Verse 2

Well I'm usually passin' by just about eleven o'clock (I never stop)
I'm usually passin' by just around eleven o'clock
And if you let cool you one time, you'll be my regular stop (Alright boys)

Chorus 3   As Chorus 2

Chorus 4   As Chorus 1

Solo

|—— 8 ——| | (Lead Guitar)

A7	A7	E7	E7	
B7	A7	E7	E7 B7	
E7	A7	E7	E7	
A7	A7	E7	E7	
B7	A7	E7	E7 B7	

Chorus 5   As Chorus 1

Chorus 6   As Chorus 1 (*vocals ad lib.*)

             N.C. | E   E7 | A   C7 | B7   (F) | E7
are guaranteed ...to satisfy....

© COPYRIGHT 1968 ARC MUSIC CORPORATION, USA.
TRISTAN MUSIC LIMITED.
ALL RIGHTS RESERVED. INTERNATIONAL COPYRIGHT SECURED.

Introduction

'Ice Cream Man', like many blues songs, can be played a lot of different ways—let's look at an arrangement based roughly on the Van Halen version. Please note that the Van Halen version is detuned a semitone.

Getting started

Start by using simple open chords, and the shuffle eighth-note strumming (see the intro to Stage 5), accenting beats 2 and 4 to bring out the groove. You really want to get a solid rhythmic foundation first.

Pay attention to the stops in the first four bars of Chorus 2 as well, which are a common blues variation. This technique is also useful for 'walking up to the IV chord' (moving from the E7 to A7) as shown in the TAB (right).

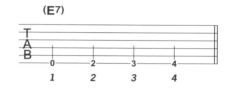

Now play the chords using a 'chunka-chunka style' shown in my *Beginner's Course* (lesson BC-183). For the B7 you'll need to use the B7 open chord and strum.

Bass line

The Van Halen acoustic guitar part starts with a cool variation using a bass line played on the beats and open thin strings played in between. The challenge is playing just the bass note and getting up to strum up on the thinnest two strings only, but like everything else it just takes practice. It's probably easier to play fingerstyle, using the thumb playing the bass and fingers on the thin strings too.

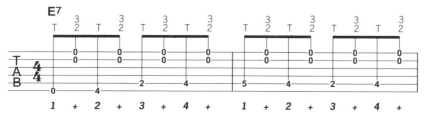

Stage 1
Stage 2
Stage 3
Stage 4
Stage 5
Stage 6
Stage 7
Stage 8
Stage 9
Bonus

I Got You (I Feel Good)

Words & Music by James Brown

♩=144

Whoa!

Verse 1

    D7   **D7**   **D7**   **D7**
I feel good,   I knew that I would, now,
     G7   **G7**   **D7**   **D7**
I feel good,   I knew that I would, now.
    A7   **G7**   **D7** **D7**
So good, so good, I got you.   (Whoa!)

Verse 2

     D7   **D7**   **D7**   **D7**
I feel nice,   like sugar and spice,
     G7   **G7**   **D7**   **D7**
I feel nice,   like sugar and spice,
    A7   **G7**   **D7** **D7**
So nice, so nice, I got you.

Link 1

| (D7) | (D7) | (D7) | (D7) |

Bridge 1

    G7   **G7**
When I hold you in my arms
 D7   **D7**
I know that I can do no wrong.
   G7   **G7**
And when I hold you in my arms
   A7   **A7**
My love won't do you no harm. (And I feel...)

Verse 3   As Verse 2

Link 2

| (D7) | (D7) | (D7) | (D7) |

Bridge 2

When I hold you in my arms
I know that I can't do no wrong.
And when I hold you in my arms
My love can't do me no harm.

Verse 4   As Verse 2

Verse 5   As Verse 1

Outro

    A7   **G7**   **D7**   **D7**
So good, so good, 'cause I got you,
    A7   **G7**   **D7** **D7** **D7**   **D7**
So good, so good, 'cause I got you.   Hey!

© COPYRIGHT 1966 FORT KNOX MUSIC COMPANY, USA.
LARK MUSIC LIMITED.
ALL RIGHTS RESERVED. INTERNATIONAL COPYRIGHT SECURED.

Introduction

This James Brown funk-soul classic can be played using conventional strumming, or by retaining the sparse guitar parts on the original recording (short 'chips' on beat 2, every second bar). It's also a great song for working on your open dominant '7' chords as we're using D7, G7 and A7.

Strumming

The 'Old Faithful' strumming pattern (see page 19) works remarkably well in this funk context—it obviously changes the feel of the song, but it's fun and a good way to help you play this song solo. During the chorus you can up the ante by strumming just the down-strums on the beats—you'll be strumming less, but creating more energy!

Solo and riff

I thought I'd include the short saxophone solo here, so that if you're playing on your own you can fill in the link, otherwise that section feels a little empty. I've written it out in open position, where you're likely to be playing the chords (so it will be easy to reach), but see you if you can move it so that it starts on fret 5—which will sound a bit more authentic.

(D7)

There's another fun lead line at the end of the choruses—it's not hard and adds another dimension to the guitar arrangement.

D7

Stage 1
Stage 2
Stage 3
Stage 4
Stage 5
Stage 6
Stage 7
Stage 8
Stage 9
Bonus

Stage 1

Stage 2

Stage 3

Stage 4

Stage 5

Stage 6

Stage 7

Stage 8

Stage 9

Bonus

Mama, Talk To Your Daughter

Words & Music by J.B. Lenoir

♩=134

Intro   ‖: G⁷ | G⁷ | G⁷ | G⁷ :‖

Verse 1

G⁷   G⁷   G⁷   G⁷
Momma, Papa, please talk to you daughter for me.
G⁷   G⁷   G⁷   G⁷
Momma, Papa, please talk to your daughter for me.
                                  G⁷   G⁷   G⁷   G⁷
She done made me love her and I ain't gonna leave her be.

Link | G⁷ | G⁷ | G⁷ | G⁷ |

Verse 2

G⁷   G⁷   G⁷   G⁷
Hey, baby, please don't dog me a - round.
C⁷   C⁷   G⁷   G⁷
Yeah, baby, please don't dog me a - round.
                      D⁷   C⁷   G⁷   G⁷
If you don't quit your fooling, put ya six feet in the ground.

Chorus 1

                      G⁷   G⁷
You should talk to your daughter,
                      G⁷   G⁷
You should talk to your daughter,
                      C⁷   C⁷
You should talk to your daughter,
                      G⁷   G⁷
You should talk to your daughter,
                      D⁷   C⁷   G⁷   G⁷
She done made me love her and I ain't gonna leave her be.

Guitar Solo   ‖: G⁷ | G⁷ | G⁷ | G⁷ |

| C⁷ | C⁷ | G⁷ | G⁷ |

| D⁷ | C⁷ | G⁷ | G⁷ :‖

| C⁷ | C⁷ | G⁷ | G⁷ |

| C⁷ | C⁷ | A⁷ | D⁷ |

Link   ‖: G⁷ | G⁷ | G⁷ | G⁷ :‖

Chorus 2   As Chorus 1 *(repeat)*

© COPYRIGHT 1968 GHANA MUSIC.
BUG MUSIC LIMITED.
ALL RIGHTS RESERVED. INTERNATIONAL COPYRIGHT SECURED.

Stage 1
Stage 2
Stage 3
Stage 4
Stage 5
Stage 6
Stage 7
Stage 8
Stage 9
Bonus

Introduction

Robben Ford is a master of modern blues and one of my favourite guitar players. This track features some incredible guitar solos, which are beyond the remit of this beginner songbook, but it's fun to jam with Robben by playing the chords along with the recording.

Structure

This is a great example of a modified blues form—up until Verse 2, the song just stays on a G7 chord, underpinning the vocals and a short guitar solo. Once the whole band kick in, the song follows a standard 12-bar blues form, except for the tail end of the guitar solo, where we have a slight departure, adding a bit more interest and some new changes for Robben to burn over!

If you're a beginner, keep the strumming simple—just down- and up-strums but with a shuffle feel—meaning that the up-strum will happen a little later than usual.

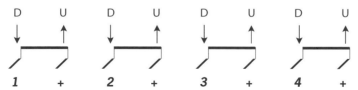

Groove

By far the best way to copy this shuffle groove is to play along with the original recording, so you can absorb the time feel—really try to emulate it and make it feel good, like you're being swept along by the rhythm. This concept of 'time feel' is such an important aspect of playing guitar, but a very hard one to explain—you just have to practise (preferably with some kind of accompaniment) and it will come. Focus on playing along with the record so you are in it, not on top of it.

More advanced players might like to check out my 'Jazz Up Your Blues' series (JA–104, free on my website) for some more advanced chord options. You'll also find a full lesson on the solo to this song in my *Blues Lead Guitar Solos* book.

Stage 1
Stage 2
Stage 3
Stage 4
Stage 5
Stage 6
Stage 7
Stage 8
Stage 9
Bonus

Mustang Sally
Words & Music by Bonny Rice

Capo
Fret
3

♩=110

Intro

| A⁷ | A⁷ | A⁷ | A⁷ | |

Verse 1

       A⁷   **A⁷**
Mustang Sally, huh, huh,
A⁷   **A⁷**   **A⁷**
  Guess you better slow your Mustang down.
   A⁷   **A⁷**   **A⁷**
Oh Lord, what I say now.

        D⁷   **D⁷**
Mustang Sally, now baby, oh Lord,
D⁷   **D⁷**   **A⁷**   **A⁷**
  Guess you better slow your Mustang down.
      A⁷   **A⁷**
Huh, oh yeah.

       E⁷   **E⁷**
You been runnin' all over town, now,
D⁷ N.C.   **(D⁷)**   **A⁷**
  Oh, I guess I have to put your flat feet on the ground.
     A⁷   **A⁷** **A⁷**
Ha, what I said, now,   listen.

Chorus 1

A⁷   **A⁷**   **A⁷**   **A⁷**
All you wanna do is ride around Sally. (Ride Sally, ride)
A⁷   **A⁷**   **A⁷**   **A⁷**
All you wanna do is ride around Sally. (Ride Sally, ride)
D⁷   **D⁷**   **D⁷**   **D⁷**
All you wanna do is ride around Sally. (Ride Sally, ride) huh.
A⁷   **A⁷**   **A⁷**   **A⁷**
All you wanna do is a-ride around Sally, oh Lord. (Ride Sally, ride.)
E⁷   **E⁷**
One of these early mornings, yeah,
D⁷ N.C.   **(D⁷)**   **A⁷**   **A⁷**
  Wow, gonna be wiping your weeping eyes, huh.
        A⁷   **A⁷**
What I said, now, look-a-here,

Verse 2

I bought you a brand new Mustang,
A nineteen-sixty-five, huh.
Now you come around, signifying a woman
You don't wanna let me ride.
Mustang Sally, now baby, oh Lord,
Guess you better slow that Mustang down, huh, oh Lord.
Listen, you been running all over town.
Ow, I got to put your flat feet on the ground, huh.
What I said now, yeah.
Let me say it one more time y'all.

Chorus 2

As Chorus 1 *(to fade)*

© COPYRIGHT 1965 (RENEWED 1993) FOURTEENTH HOUR MUSIC AND SPRINGTIME MUSIC INC.
ALL RIGHTS FOR THE WORLD EXCLUDING THE U.S. AND CANADA CONTROLLED AND ADMINISTERED
BY EMI MUSIC PUBLISHING LTD.
ALL RIGHTS RESERVED. INTERNATIONAL COPYRIGHT SECURED.

Stage 1
Stage 2
Stage 3
Stage 4
Stage 5
Stage 6
Stage 7
Stage 8
Stage 9
Bonus

Introduction

This popular singalong tune, famously recorded by Wilson Pickett, has just three chords and follows a kind of extended blues form. To perform it, you'll really need to focus on the groove, and on your strumming. We're going to play it with a capo at fret 3, though Wilson Pickett's version is in C, and uses barre chords, mixed with little melodies and riffs.

Strumming

The chords are straightforward, and I'd recommend using '7' chords throughout, although you can use standard major chords as well. Try the strumming pattern below—it captures the vibe of the recording pretty well, but experiment with it, and see how you might want to adapt it.

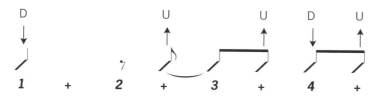

Stops

The stops are crucial to the arrangement—you'll see them marked by 'N.C.' (No Chord). Strum the chord on beat 1 and then stop the chord ringing out by touching the strings with the outside of your strumming hand on beat 2 and don't play for the rest of that bar and the next.

Secondly, if you're playing it on your own you might like to develop the rhythm pattern in the chorus, adding more strums, just to give it some extra interest—if you play it the same all the way through it can get a bit monotonous for the listener.

Stage 1
Stage 2
Stage 3
Stage 4
Stage 5
Stage 6
Stage 7
Stage 8
Stage 9
Bonus

Rock Around The Clock

Words & Music by Max C. Freedman & Jimmy De Knight

♩=182

Intro

(N.C)   A⁷
One, two, three o'clock, four o'clock, rock,

(N.C)   A⁷
Five, six, seven o'clock, eight o'clock, rock,

(N.C)
Nine, ten, eleven o'clock, twelve o'clock, rock,

      E⁷   E⁷
We're gonna rock around the clock tonight.

Verse 1

     A⁷   A⁷
Put your glad rags on and join me, hon,

   A⁷   A⁷
We'll have some fun when the clock strikes one,

      D⁷   D⁷
We're gonna rock around the clock tonight,

      A⁷   A⁷
We're gonna rock, rock, rock, 'til broad daylight

      E⁷   E⁷   A⁷ A⁷
We're gonna rock, gonna rock, a - round the clock to - night.

Verse 2

When the clock strikes two, three and four,
If the band slows down we'll yell for more,
We're gonna rock around the clock tonight,
We're gonna rock, rock, rock, 'til broad daylight
We're gonna rock, gonna rock, around the clock tonight.

Guitar solo

A⁷	A⁷	A⁷	A⁷
D⁷	D⁷	A⁷	A⁷
E⁷	E⁷	A⁷	A⁷

Verse 3

When the chimes ring five, six and seven,
We'll be right in seventh heaven.
We're gonna rock around the clock tonight,
We're gonna rock, rock, rock, 'til broad daylight
We're gonna rock, gonna rock, around the clock tonight.

Verse 4

When it's eight, nine, ten, eleven too,
I'll be goin' strong and so will you.
We're gonna rock around the clock tonight,
We're gonna rock, rock, rock, 'til broad daylight
We're gonna rock, gonna rock, around the clock tonight.

Instrumental As Guitar Solo

Verse 5

When the clock strikes twelve, we'll cool off then,
Start a-rockin' round the clock again.
We're gonna rock around the clock tonight,
We're gonna rock, rock, rock, 'til broad daylight
We're gonna rock, gonna rock, around the clock tonight.

Outro

| A A⁷ | D Dm | A | | E A | A⁷ |

A
××× ⌢
①① 5fr
②

D
××× ⌢
①① 10fr
②

E
××× ⌢
①① 12fr
②

© COPYRIGHT 1953 MYERS-MUSIC.
KASSNER ASSOCIATED PUBLISHERS LIMITED.
ALL RIGHTS RESERVED. INTERNATIONAL COPYRIGHT SECURED.

Stage 1
Stage 2
Stage 3
Stage 4
Stage 5
Stage 6
Stage 7
Stage 8
Stage 9
Bonus

 Introduction

This Bill Haley classic is simple but has a few really useful skills to impart that will help you out in many musical situations.

Strumming

The intro has an interesting accented rhythm. When Bill says 'One', that's beat 1 of the bar, where you hit the A7 chord and then 'rest'. Keep counting until the '+' after 3 of the next bar, where two more 'hits' are played. On the E7 chords, 'hit' on beats 2 and 4.

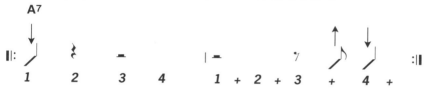

Once we get into the song you can use any number of strumming patterns—just playing regular eighth-notes with a bit of a shuffle rhythm will work well, and you could even use a 'chunka-chunka' shuffle (see my lesson BC-183) if you want.

Mini barre chords

On the recording you'll hear a lead guitar part, playing 'mini barre' chords on the thinnest three strings. If you're feeling brave, give them a go (grips are all on the song sheet page), using the rhythm below. You should leave them loose on the neck, and just press down and quickly release the grip after strumming.

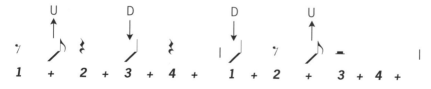

Smokestack Lightning

Words & Music by Chester Burnette

Stage 1
Stage 2
Stage 3
Stage 4
Stage 5
Stage 6
Stage 7
Stage 8
Stage 9
Bonus

♩=144

riff

Intro | (E) | (E)   ‖: E | E   :‖

Verse 1
cont. riff
Ah-oh, smokestack lightnin',
Shinin', just like gold,
Why don't ya hear me cryin'?
A-whoo-hoo, whoo, whoo.

Verse 2
Whoa-oh, tell me, baby,
What's the matter with you?
Why don't ya hear me cryin'?
Whoo-hoooo, whoo-hoo, whoo.

Harmonica solo | (E) | (E) | (E) | (E) | (E) | (E) |

Verse 3
Whoa-oh, tell me, baby,
Where did ya stay last night?
A-why don't ya hear me cryin'?
Whoo-hoo, whoo-hoo, whoo.

Verse 4
Whoa-oh, stop your train,
Let her go for a ride.
Why don't ya hear me cryin'?
Whoo-hoo, whoo-hoo, whoo.

Harmonica solo 2 | (E) | (E) | (E) | (E) | (E) | (E) |

Verse 5
Whoa-oh, fare ya well.
Never see, a-you no more.
A-why don't ya hear me cryin'?
Whoo-hoo, whoo-hoo, whoo.

Verse 6
Whoa-oh, who been here baby since,
I-I been gone, a little, bity boy?
Girl, be on.
A-whoo-hoo, whoo-hoo, whoo.

To fade

© COPYRIGHT 1956 ARC MUSIC CORPORATION, USA.
JEWEL MUSIC PUBLISHING COMPANY LIMITED.
ALL RIGHTS RESERVED. INTERNATIONAL COPYRIGHT SECURED.

Stage 1

Stage 2

Stage 3

Stage 4

Stage 5

Stage 6

Stage 7

Stage 8

Stage 9

Bonus

 Introduction

This is one of the finest blues riffs of all time and really fun to play—it's a little tricky but I know you're going to love it! We're looking at the original recording by Howlin' Wolf.

 Playing the riff

This arrangement uses a consistent bass note on the beat but the original version is a bit more random, and therefore harder to teach precisely. Start with this standardized version and listen to the original a lot to 'loosen up' your playing!

The aim is to use your thumb to play the open E bass note on the beat, while playing the melody riff with your fingers. It's going to take some practice and it will take some getting used to. Practise it slowly.

Start by playing just the bass very slowly, and add the first melody notes of the riff. When you're happy with that, play the next bass note, and then add the next two melody notes. Grow it into the full riff, little by little.

Use the fingers you find most comfortable—I use fingers 2 and 3 for the double-stop (when two melody notes are played together), and finger 2 for the rest of the notes except for the D (string 2, fret 3), for which I use finger 1.

 Riff

To get the right sound on the double-stop you should bend the notes up just a bit—not a proper string-bend, a 'curl' (a quarter-tone), just to make it cry a little!

113

Walking The Dog

Words & Music by Rufus Thomas

Stage 1
Stage 2
Stage 3
Stage 4
Stage 5
Stage 6
Stage 7
Stage 8
Stage 9
Bonus

♩=122

Intro

| **A7**　　| **A7**　　|　　|

Verse 1

　A7　　　　　　　　**A7**
　Baby's back, dressed in black,
　A7　　　　　　　　　　**A7**
　Silver buttons all down her back.
　A7　　　　　**A7**
　Hi-ho, tip-to-toes,
　A7　　　　　　　　　　　　**A7**
She broke the needle and she can't sew.

Chorus 1

　　　　　　　　　D7
Walkin' the dog,
D7　　　　　　　　　　　**A7**　　**A7**
　I'm just a-walkin' the dog.
　　　　　　E7
If you don't know how to do it,
　　D7　　　　　　　　　　　**A7**　　**E7**
I'll show you how to walk the dog.

Verse 2

I asked her mother for fifteen cents,
Seen the elephant jump the fence.
He jumped so high he touched the sky,
Didn't get back till a quarter to five.

Chorus 2

As Chorus 1

Verse 3

Tell me Mary, quite contrary,
How does your garden grow?
What with silver bells and cockleshells,
And pretty maids all in a row.

Chorus 3

As Chorus 1

Guitar Solo

A7	**A7**	**A7**	**A7**
D7	**D7**	**A7**	**A7**
E7	**D7**	**A7**	**E7**

Verse 4

As Verse 1

Chorus 4

As Chorus 1

Outro

　　　　　　　A7　　　**A7**　　　　　**A7**　　**A7**　　　　　**D7**　　　**D7**
(stuttering)　　Yeah!　　Oh, just a walkin',　　oh, just a walkin',
　　　　　　　A7　　　**A7**
Oh, just a walkin',
||:　　　**E7**
　　If you don't know how to do it,
　　D7　　　　　　　　　　　**A7**　　**A7** :|| (Play x3)
I'll show you how to walk the dog.

RONDOR MUSIC (LONDON) LIMITED.
ALL RIGHTS RESERVED. INTERNATIONAL COPYRIGHT SECURED.

Introduction

This classic blues, covered by The Rolling Stones is a kind of 16-bar blues, a fairly common development of the 12-bar blues.

Part 1 – Brian

There are two distinct parts on the Rolling Stones recording: the first is Brian Jones playing 'Old Faithful', using open chords—nothing too complicated. Watch out for the little rhythmic figure on the E7 at the end of the chorus and guitar solo. It should be quite easy to copy.

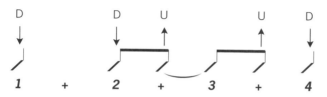

Part 2 – Keith

Keith Richard's part is an interesting adventure, beyond beginner level but worth revisiting later, or a fun diversion if you want to test yourself!

The main riff on the A7 is shown below. Start by playing the open A (string 5) on the beat and then use fingers 2 and 1 to play the next two notes. Be careful not to hit the other strings, and to get the slide from just a few frets below the shown note. Then you'll shift back and slide up to fret 6 with finger 2 and finish with finger 1 on fret 5.

The riff has a similar pattern for the D7 and E7, but with different open strings, and your fretting fingers form a different shape. If these riffs are too challenging you can just stick with playing D7 and E7 chords.

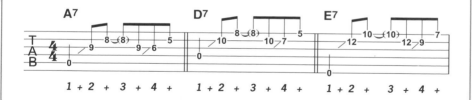

Stage 1
Stage 2
Stage 3
Stage 4
Stage 5
Stage 6
Stage 7
Stage 8
Stage 9
Bonus

You Never Can Tell

Words & Music by Chuck Berry

Capo Fret **3**

♩=158

Intro | A | E⁷ |

Verse 1

(E⁷)   A   A   A   A
It was a teenage wedding and the old folks wished them well,
       A   A   E⁷   E⁷
You could see that Pierre did truly love the mademoi - selle.
      E⁷   E⁷   E⁷
And now the young monsieur and ma - dame have rung the chapel bell,
    E⁷   E⁷   A   E⁷
'C'est la vie.' say the old folks, it goes to show you never can tell.

Verse 2

They furnished off an apartment with a two room Roebuck sale,
The coolerator was crammed with TV dinners and ginger ale.
But when Pierre found work, the little money coming worked out well,
'C'est la vie.' say the old folks, it goes to show you never can tell.

Verse 3

They had a hi-fi phono, boy, did they let it blast,
Seven hundred little records, all rock, rhythm and jazz.
But when the sun went down, the rapid tempo of the music fell,
'C'est la vie.' say the old folks, it goes to show you never can tell.

Verse 4

They bought a souped-up Jitney, 'twas a cherry red 'fifty-three,
And drove it down to Orleans to celebrate their anniversary.
It was there where Pierre was wedded to the lovely mademoiselle,
'C'est la vie.' say the old folks, it goes to show you never can tell.

Instrumental

A	A	A	A
A	A	E⁷	E⁷
E⁷	E⁷	E⁷	E⁷
E⁷	E⁷	A	E⁷

Verse 5   As Verse 1

Outro

| A | A | A | A |
| A | A | E⁷ | E⁷ | *Fade*

© COPYRIGHT 1964 ARC MUSIC CORPORATION, USA.
TRISTAN MUSIC LIMITED.
ALL RIGHTS RESERVED. INTERNATIONAL COPYRIGHT SECURED.

Introduction

Not only was Chuck Berry a fantastic and massively influential guitar player—he could write hit songs with pretty minimal resources!

 Capo

For this song you should place your capo on fret 3 and you'll use just your A and E7 chord grips. Remember that you only need the capo if you want to play along with the original recording (which I recommend because it's great fun).

 Strumming

Start by playing four down-strums per bar and make sure you can play through the chord changes without having to stop. Play along with the record, and make sure your chord changes are really smooth. Let's face it—there are not a lot of chord changes in this song, so you should be able to really focus on them.

If you want to make the strumming more complex, you can add up-strums (as shown below), but be aware that when you are playing a chord change the very last up-strum will often just be open strings as you transition between chords—and that is totally fine!

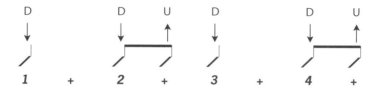

Stage 1
Stage 2
Stage 3
Stage 4
Stage 5
Stage 6
Stage 7
Stage 8
Stage 9
Bonus

Bad To The Bone
Words & Music by George Thorogood

♩=100

⑥ = D	③ = G
⑤ = G	② = B
④ = D	① = D

Riff throughout

‖: (G5)   G5 G5 C5 G5 B♭5 :‖

Intro
Play riff x7

Verse 1
(clean tone)
On the day I was born, the nurses all I gathered 'round
And they gazed in wide wonder, at the joy they had found.
The head nurse spoke up, said 'Leave this one alone!'
She could tell right away that I was bad to the bone.

Chorus 1
(w/distortion)
Bad to the bone, bad to the bone.
B-B-B-B-Bad to the bone.
B-B-B-B-Bad, B-B-B-B-Bad, bad to the bone.

Verse 2
I broke a thousand hearts, before I met you.
I'll break a thousand more, baby, before I am through.
I wanna be yours pretty baby, yours and yours alone.
w/distortion
I'm here to tell ya honey,   that I'm bad to the bone.

Chorus 2
As Chorus 1 *(Vocals ad lib.)*

Solo 1

‖: w/riff | w/riff | w/riff | w/riff :‖ *(Play x3)*

| G5 | |

Verse 3
N.C   w/riff
I make a rich woman beg, I'll make a good woman steal.
I'll make an old woman blush, and make a young girl squeal.
I wanna be yours pretty baby, yours and yours alone.
I'm here to tell ya honey, that I'm bad to the bone.

Chorus 3
As Chorus 1 *(Vocals ad lib.)*

Solo 2

‖: w/riff | w/riff | w/riff | w/riff :‖ *(Play x8)*

Verse 4
And when I walk the streets, Kings and Queens step aside.
Every woman I meet, they all stay satisfied.
I wanna tell ya pretty baby, well ya see I make my own.
I'm here to tell ya honey, that I'm bad to the bone.

Chorus 4
As Chorus 1 *(Vocals ad lib.)*

Outro
(Play x3)

‖: w/riff | w/riff | w/riff | w/riff :‖ G5

© COPYRIGHT 1982 DEL SOUND MUSIC.
UNIVERSAL/MCA MUSIC LIMITED.
ALL RIGHTS IN GERMANY ADMINISTERED BY UNIVERSAL/MCA MUSIC PUBL. GMBH.
ALL RIGHTS RESERVED. INTERNATIONAL COPYRIGHT SECURED.

Introduction

This massive hit for George Thorogood is a lot of fun to play and gives you a little insight into open G tuning, as well as slide guitar playing.

Open G tuning

I have a full lesson on this topic (ES-031) on my website, but essentially you need to tune strings 6, 5 and 1 down a tone, leaving you with the notes of a G chord—so playing all the strings with no fingers down will give you a G chord! This tuning is very common in traditional blues music, and is used by a lot of the blues rock masters, most notably Keith Richards. Other than using a tuner, the easiest way to achieve open G tuning is to use string 4 (the note D) as a reference to tune the two outside E strings down a tone. Then use string 3 (the note G) as a reference to tune string 5 down a tone.

Chords in open G are usually played by barring all the way across the strings, so to get a C chord you would barre the 5th fret, and for a B♭ chord you would barre the 3rd fret. Note that you usually do not play the thickest string when playing these chords (ever wondered why Keith Richards played his famous 5-string Telecaster? He took off the thickest string when playing in open G because he never used it!).

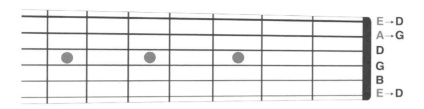

E→D
A→G
D
G
B
E→D

Stage 1
Stage 2
Stage 3
Stage 4
Stage 5
Stage 6
Stage 7
Stage 8
Stage 9
Bonus

Stage 1 Stage 2 Stage 3 Stage 4 Stage 5 Stage 6 Stage 7 Stage 8 Stage 9 Bonus

Riff

For the riff, play open strings for the G chord, barre on fret 5 for the C chord and barre on fret 3 for the B♭. See the TAB below and give it shot—just fret with finger 1 for now. The rhythm uses triplets (BC-155), which we looked at in the introduction to this stage, and means that each beat is divided into three shorter beats.

When playing the riff make sure you get the rhythm right—count it if you like, but it's easier just to listen to it quite a few times, as it's pretty much the same through the whole song!

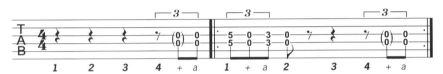

You can play this riff using a slide as well, as per the original recording. The slide will take the place of your finger barre—see below for tips on slide guitar playing.

Slide guitar

If you want to get started with slide guitar here are my handy hints:

* Put the slide on finger 3 or 4, whichever is most comfortable.

* Don't press too hard—the slide should NOT touch the neck at all.

* Use fingers 1 and 2 to lightly press behind the slide, muting any unwanted vibrations. You'll also need to mute any strings that you don't want to play, using your strumming hand.

* Nearly all slide players play with their fingers (not a pick) to keep the strings under control.

Look up my 'Slide Guitar Basics' lesson (TE-801) online to see all of these techniques in action.

Stage 5: Final notes

Are there any songs or techniques that you want to revisit later in the course? Write them down!

Stage 1

Stage 2

Stage 3

Stage 4

Stage 5

Stage 6

Stage 7

Stage 8

Stage 9

Bonus

Introduction

This stage introduces the F chord, which is the chord that most guitarists really struggle with. I certainly did, and used to avoid any songs that had an F chord in them… but you can't avoid it forever, so it's best to just confront your fears, get stuck in and try out some of these songs. It only takes practice! I know it can feel impossible, and that you will never get it right, but it is easier than it first feels. It takes a bit of time to build up the necessary strength in your fingers to hold the chord correctly, and then to get the changes to and from it as well. Make sure you keep up the One-Minute Changes (BC-162).

Chord extensions

In this stage, I've also decided to introduce a few chord 'extensions'. This means you may see some chords with the suffix 'm7' or 'add9' or various other combinations of numbers! Some of these chords will be properly introduced later, while some are outside what I cover in the *Beginner's Course*. However, I must emphasise that they are not difficult chords to play—if they were difficult then I wouldn't have included them at all! Playing these 'outsider' chords will allow you to learn some great songs, which simply wouldn't sound right if they were played another way. So don't be put off by any complex-sounding chord names—follow the lesson and the accompanying chord diagrams and you'll be fine.

Stage 1
Stage 2
Stage 3
Stage 4
Stage 5
Stage 6
Stage 7
Stage 8
Stage 9
Bonus

Stage 6 Chords

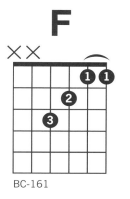

BC-161

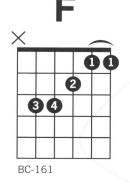

BC-161

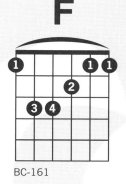

BC-161

 Stage 6: Your notes

Ain't No Sunshine

Words & Music by Bill Withers

♩=80

Verse 1

N.C | Am⁷   Em⁷ G⁷ |
Ain't no sunshine when she's   gone,

Am⁷ | Am⁷   Em⁷ G⁷ |
    It's not warm when she's a - way,

Am⁷   Em⁷⁽²⁾
    Ain't no sunshine when she's gone,

               Dm⁷
And she always gone too long,

             | Am⁷   Em⁷ G⁷ |
Anytime she goes a - way.

Verse 2

I wonder this time where she's gone,
I wonder if she's gone to stay,
Ain't no sunshine when she's gone,
And this house just ain't no home,
Anytime she goes away.

Bridge

Am⁷ |(Am⁷)
    And I know, I know, I know, I know, I know...

| (Am⁷) | (Am⁷) | (Am⁷) | (Am⁷) |

                           (Am⁷)
Hey, I oughta leave the young thing a - lone but

             |Am⁷   Em⁷   G⁷ |
Ain't no sunshine when she's gone, whoa.

Verse 3

Ain't no sunshine when she's gone,
Only darkness every day,
Ain't no sunshine when she's gone,
And this house just ain't no home,
Anytime she goes away,
Anytime she goes away,
Anytime she goes away,
Anytime she goes away.

© COPYRIGHT 1971 INTERIOR MUSIC CORPORATION.
UNIVERSAL/MCA MUSIC LIMITED.
ALL RIGHTS RESERVED. INTERNATIONAL COPYRIGHT SECURED.

Stage 1
Stage 2
Stage 3
Stage 4
Stage 5
Stage 6
Stage 7
Stage 8
Stage 9
Bonus

justinguitar.com

Stage 1
Stage 2
Stage 3
Stage 4
Stage 5
Stage 6
Stage 7
Stage 8
Stage 9
Bonus

 # Introduction

Bill Withers' hit from 1971 is simply a great song—it's one of those classics that's perfect for beginners because you can keep it simple, using nice easy chords and simple rhythms, and then as you improve as a player you can add more complex chords and melody lines.

 # Basic chords

To keep things easy initially, I recommend that you simplify the chords to Am, Dm, Em, and G. Forget the '7' chord extensions for the moment, while you nail down the basics.

To start with, play each chord once. You still want to count the right number of beats on each chord (initially, two counts on the Am and one each on the Em and G), but hopefully your ears will help you with that. Then try strumming on every beat, and you can also try out the original, more complex chord voicings shown below.

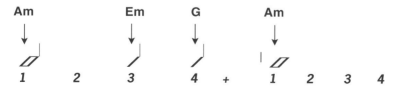

Advanced chords

In order to find out exactly Bill Withers played the chords, I referenced a great live version of the song (on YouTube) with him sporting an orange roll neck sweater. Here he plays the guitar fingerstyle with his thumb playing the bass notes and fingers playing the chords—but you could just use the video as inspiration and interpret the song differently. If the vocal is strong, you are (pretty much) free to play what you like on the guitar!

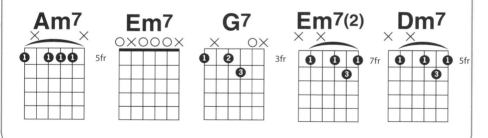

Counting Stars

Words & Music by Ryan Tedder

Capo Fret 4

♩=122

Intro Chorus

```
Am              C
Lately I've been, I've been losing sleep,
G                                F
    Dreaming about the things that we could be.
    Am           C
But baby, I've been, I've been praying hard,
G                                F
    Said no more counting dollars, we'll be counting stars,
F                          (Am)
    Yeah, we'll be counting stars.
```

Link 1

```
‖: Am    | C      | G      | F      :‖
```

Verse 1

I see this life like a swinging vine, swing my heart across the line,
In my face is flashing signs, seek it out and ye shall find.
Old, but I'm not that old, young, but I'm not that bold,
And I don't think the world is sold, I'm just doing what we're told.

Pre-chorus 1

```
Am   C                  G              F
 I     feel something so right by doing the wrong thing,
Am      C              G                F
   And I,   feel something so wrong by doing the right thing.
F                     F
   I couldn't lie, couldn't lie, couldn't lie,
F              F                   (Am)
Everything that kills me makes me feel alive.
```

Chorus 2

Lately I've been, I've been losing sleep,
Dreaming about the things that we could be.
But baby, I've been, I've been praying hard,
Said no more counting dollars, we'll be counting stars.
Lately I've been, I've been losing sleep,
Dreaming about the things that we could be.
But baby, I've been, I've been praying hard,
Said no more counting dollars, we'll be, we'll be counting stars.

Link 2

```
| Am    | C      | G      | F      |
```

Verse 2

I feel the love and I feel it burn down this river every turn,
Hope is our four letter word, make that money, watch it burn.
Old, but I'm not that old, young, but I'm not that bold,
And I don't think the world is sold, I'm just doing what we're told.

Pre-chorus 2

```
Am      C              G                F
   And I  feel something so wrong by doing the right thing.
F                     F
   I couldn't lie, couldn't lie, couldn't lie,
F              F
Everything that drowns me makes me wanna fly.
```

© COPYRIGHT 2013 SONY ATV SONGS LLC/MIDNITE MIRACLE MUSIC.
SONY/ATV MUSIC PUBLISHING.
ALL RIGHTS RESERVED. INTERNATIONAL COPYRIGHT SECURED.

Stage 1 · Stage 2 · Stage 3 · Stage 4 · Stage 5 · Stage 6 · Stage 7 · Stage 8 · Stage 9 · Bonus

justinguitar.com

Stage 1
Stage 2
Stage 3
Stage 4
Stage 5
Stage 6
Stage 7
Stage 8
Stage 9
Bonus

Chorus 3	As Chorus 2

Bridge

N.C. (Am.)
‖: Oh, take that money watch it burn,
Sink in the river, the lessons I learned. :‖ (x4)
F　　　　　　**Dm**
Everything that kills me makes me feel alive.

Chorus 4	As Chorus 2

**Outro
Chorus**

‖: Take that money watch it burn,
Sink in the river, the lessons I learned. :‖ (x4)

 ## Introduction

This was one of the biggest hits of 2013, released by the band OneRepublic.

 ## Strumming

There are quite a few different ways to play this song. It's essentially the same four chords repeated throughout the song—Am, C G and F (and a sneaky Dm in the bridge)—so it's not too challenging, although you'll need to use a capo on fret 4 to play at the correct pitch. There are a few stops and a few occasions where you should play a chord and let it ring—if you listen to the original recording, you'll pick these up. In order to familiarise yourself with the structure, I'd recommend starting off playing just four down-strums per bar.

When you listen to the song, you'll hear quiet fingerstyle moments alongside more full-on strumming. For the quieter sections, you will probably want to stick to very simple strumming or the fingerstyle pattern (on the next page), while the constant down-strum pattern below will work better for the more energetic sections. You'll find that playing a little harder on beats 2 and 4 will accentuate the groove.

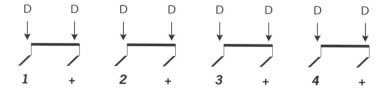

continued...

127

Stage 1

Stage 2

Stage 3

Stage 4

Stage 5

Stage 6

Stage 7

Stage 8

Stage 9

Bonus

✸ Intro – fingerstyle

There is a cool fingerstyle pattern which appears in the intro and later on in the song, which you can apply to the open chords (below), still using a capo. Your thumb will play the bass note of the chord (the lowest note, either string 5 or string 6), then finger 1 will play string 4. Next, fingers 2 and 3 will pick strings 3 and 2, then finger 1 will play string 4 again. This pattern is repeated twice each bar.

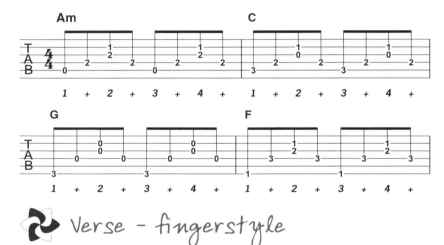

✸ Verse – fingerstyle

In the verses it's simplified a bit—play the bass note on each beat and then the chord with all three fingers on the off beats.

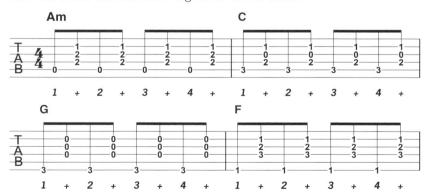

When you're confident with your barre chords, take the capo off and give them a try. The chords will now be: C#m, E, B and A. I recommend playing them all with a root 6 shape (E shape) except the E which will be root 5 (A shape). The one-off bridge chord becomes F#m.

Let Her Go
Words & Music by Michael Rosenberg

Stage 1
Stage 2
Stage 3
Stage 4
Stage 5
Stage 6
Stage 7
Stage 8
Stage 9
Bonus

 ## Introduction

I love this song by Passenger, which includes a fantastic fingerstyle guitar part as well. I've been teaching this song for a while now online—long before this book was even a twinkle in my publisher's eye!

 ## Fingerstyle or strumming?

The main fingerstyle pattern in this song is pretty tricky but it's lovely to play and well worth the effort of learning it—but the song works brilliantly in many different arrangements (they say that's the mark of a really well-written song), and so you'll enjoy playing it no matter what your ability!

Whichever arrangement you choose to focus on, I recommend starting with very simple down-strums on the beat—as per usual—until you are familiar with the chord changes and the structure of the song.

Once you're comfortable with that you might like to try out 'Old Faithful' (see page 19) which will work pretty well.

 ## Strumming

You'll get closer to the original rhythm by strumming even eighth-note up- and down-strums and including accents as shown below.

 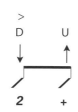 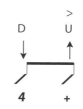

Occasionally (usually on the G chord at the end of the verse and chorus) there is a 'delayed beat 1' accent, which coincides with the chord change, so you'll change chords half a beat later than you would expect.

Let Her Go

Words & Music by Michael Rosenberg

Capo Fret 7

♩=150

Intro

F	F G	Am	G
F	F G	Am	Am G
F	F G	Am	G
F	F G	Am

Chorus 1

   Am   G   F   C
Well, you only need the light when it's burning low,

              G   Am
Only miss the sun when it starts to snow,

           F   C   G
Only know you love her when you let her go.

G   F   C
  Only know you've been high when you're feeling low,

            G   Am
Only hate the road when you're missing home,

           F   C   G
Only know you love her when you let her go,

G
  And you let her go.

Link 1

| Am | Fmaj⁷ | G | Em |
| Am | Fmaj⁷ | G | G |

Verse 1

Am   Fmaj⁷
Staring at the bottom of your glass,

        G   Em
Hoping one day you'll make a dream last,

               Am   Fmaj⁷ G   G
But dreams come slow and they go so fast.

     Am   Fmaj⁷
You see her when you close your eyes,

       G   Em
Maybe one day you'll understand why

               Am   Fmaj⁷   G   G
Everything you touch surely dies.

Chorus 2

                    Fmaj⁷   C
But you only need the light when it's burning low,

              G   Am
Only miss the sun when it starts to snow,

              Fmaj⁷   C   G
Only know you love her when you let her go.

G   Fmaj⁷   C
  Only know you've been high when you're feeling low,

            G   Am
Only hate the road when you're missing home,

© COPYRIGHT 2012 SONY/ATV MUSIC PUBLISHING.
ALL RIGHTS RESERVED. INTERNATIONAL COPYRIGHT SECURED.

Stage 1
Stage 2
Stage 3
Stage 4
Stage 5
Stage 6
Stage 7
Stage 8
Stage 9
Bonus

               Fmaj7   **C**   **G**   **G**

Only know you love her when you let her go.

Verse 2

Staring at the ceiling in the dark,
Same old empty feeling in your heart
'Cause love comes slow and it goes so fast.
Well, you see her when you fall asleep,
But never to touch and never to keep,
'Cause you loved her too much and you dived too deep.

Chorus 3

As Chorus 2

                   Am   **Fmaj7** **G** **G**

And you let her go, oh, oh, oh no.   *(Play x2)*
Will you let her go?

Instr.

| Am | Fmaj7 | G | Em |
| Am | Fmaj7 | G | G |

Chorus 4

As Chorus 2

Fingerstyle – intro

Here is the intro to the song—it's really quite tricky, so if you even manage a bar of two of it, you'll have done very well! I'd recommend coming back to this to at the end of the *Beginner's Course*.

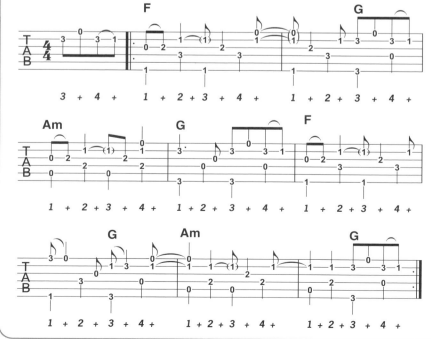

131

Hotel California

Words & Music by Don Henley, Don Felder & Glenn Frey

Capo Fret **7**

♩=148

Intro

‖: Em | Em | B7 | B7 | D | D | A | A |

| C | C | G | G | Am | Am | B7 | B7 :‖

Verse 1

Em   Em   B7   B7
  On a dark desert highway,   cool wind in my hair,
D   D   A   A
  Warm smell of colitas   rising up through the air.
C   C   G   G
  Up ahead in the distance   I saw a shimmering light,
Am   Am   B7
  My head grew heavy and my sight grew dim,
                  B7
I had to stop for the night.

Verse 2

There she stood in the doorway, I heard the mission bell
And I was thinking to myself,
This could be Heaven and this could be Hell.
Then she lit up a candle and she showed me the way,
There were voices down the corridor,
I thought I heard them say.

Chorus 1

C   C   G   G
  Welcome to the Hotel Cali - fornia,
     B7   B7   Em   Em
Such a lovely place, (such a lovely place), such a lovely face.
C   C   G   G
Plenty of room at the Hotel Cali - fornia,
    Am   Am   B7   B7
Any time of year, (any time of year), you can find it here.

Verse 3

Her mind is Tiffany-twisted, she got the Mercedes bends,
She got a lot of pretty, pretty boys she calls friends.
How they dance in the courtyard, sweet summer sweat,
Some dance to remember, some dance to forget.

Verse 4

So I called up the Captain, please bring me my wine,
He said, we haven't had that spirit here since nineteen-sixty-nine.
And still those voices are calling from far away,
Wake you up in the middle of the night just to hear them say.

Chorus 2

Welcome to the Hotel California,
Such a lovely place, (such a lovely place), such a lovely face.
They living it up at the Hotel California,
What a nice surprise, (what a nice surprise), bring your alibis.

Verse 5

Mirrors on the ceiling, the pink champagne on ice,
And she said, we are all just prisoners here of our own device.
And in the master's chambers they gathered for the feast,
They stab it with their steely knives, but they just can't kill the beast.

© COPYRIGHT 1976 & 1977 RED CLOUD MUSIC/FINGERS MUSIC/CASS COUNTY MUSIC CO.
UNIVERSAL/MCA MUSIC LIMITED/WARNER/CHAPPELL NORTH AMERICA LIMITED.
ALL RIGHTS RESERVED. INTERNATIONAL COPYRIGHT SECURED.

Verse 6　　Last thing I remember, I was running for the door,
　　　　　　　I had to find the passage back to the place I was before.
　　　　　　　Relax, said the night man, we are programmed to receive,
　　　　　　　You can check-out any time you like, but you can never leave.

Outro　　Chords as Intro *(Repeat x5 to fade)*

 # Introduction

This Eagles classic is one of the greatest recordings of all time and a really fun tune for beginners. The song uses a capo at the 7th fret, giving the guitar a really bright, chiming sound.

 # Picking and strumming

The original recording of the intro is pretty complex—picking one note at a time from the chords and adding embellishments—so I would recommend strumming the intro for now.

Get familiar with the chord changes, as usual, and then try this strumming pattern. Practise it until it feels and sounds relaxed; if you get tense it will sound awkward!

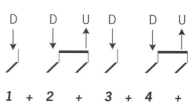

A nice variation is to change it into a two-bar strumming pattern—this works really well in the verses.

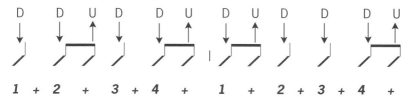

You can also try playing even eighth-notes during the chorus to pick the energy up—adding extra strums during the chorus will really help define the song sections and make it more dramatic for the listener.

Stage 1
Stage 2
Stage 3
Stage 4
Stage 5
Stage 6
Stage 7
Stage 8
Stage 9
Bonus

I'm Not The Only One

Words & Music by James Napier & Sam Smith

Capo
Fret
5

♩=82

Intro

| C E7 | Am F | C E7 | Am F |
| C E7 | Am F | C F | C |

Verse 1

|C E7 * |Am F |
You and me, we made a vow,

|C E7 * |Am F |
For better or for worse.

|C E7 * |Am F
I can't believe you let me down,

|C F |C
But the proof's in the way it hurts.

Verse 2

For months on end I've had my doubts,
Denyng every tear.
I wish this would be over now,
But I know that I still need you here.

Chorus 1

|C E7 |Am F
You say I'm crazy

|C E7 |Am F
'Cause you don't think I know what you've done,

|C E7 |Am C F
But when you call me baby,

|C Fadd9 |C Fadd9 |
I know I'm not the only one.

Verse 3

You've been so unavailable,
Now sadly I know why.
Your heart is unobtainable,
Even though Lord knows you kept mine.

Chorus 2

As Chorus 1

Bridge

Fmaj7 C
I have loved you for many years,

E7 |Am C |
Maybe I am just not e - nough.

F C
You've made me realise my deepest fear,

Fadd9 Fadd9
By lying and tearing us up.

Chorus 3

As Chorus 1 *(Play x2)*

Outro Chorus

I know I'm not the only one, I know I'm not the only one.
And I know, and I know, and I know
And I know, and I know, and I know, no,
I know I'm not the only one.

Fadd9

Stage 1
Stage 2
Stage 3
Stage 4
Stage 5
Stage 6
Stage 7
Stage 8
Stage 9
Bonus

© COPYRIGHT 2014 STELLAR SONGS LIMITED/NAUGHTY WORDS LIMITED/SALLI ISAAK SONGS LIMITED.
UNIVERSAL MUSIC PUBLISHING LIMITED/EMI MUSIC PUBLISHING LIMITED/SONY/ATV MUSIC PUBLISHING.
ALL RIGHTS RESERVED. INTERNATIONAL COPYRIGHT SECURED

Stage 1
Stage 2
Stage 3
Stage 4
Stage 5
Stage 6
Stage 7
Stage 8
Stage 9
Bonus

Introduction

This mega hit from Sam Smith is in F major—not the friendliest key for guitarists, so in this version we'll be using a capo so we can play open chords. I have a lesson on the original version on my website if you want to check it out once you've nailed your barre chords!

Easy strumming & counting

The chord sequence is very similar throughout the song, with a small variation every four bars and then a bridge section. Also, you can play the F chords with a small Fmaj7 grip which is a lot easier than the full F barre chord. You'll also see an Fadd9 chord, the grip for which is on the song sheet.

I recommend starting simply, just playing four down-strums to the bar, learning to play along with the original recording. After that, experiment with the rhythm—the pattern below shows the chord changes as they appear on the recording. As you'll see, there's a noticeable 'push' on the Am and F chords (marked on the song sheet with a *)—practise these slowly, and get them right!

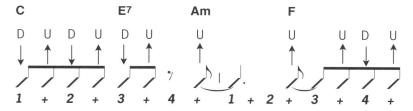

The bridge

The bridge section starts with a tasty Fmaj7 followed by chords that we've seen in the song already. As usual with a bridge, you should make the song different dynamically, perhaps playing a bit softer— maybe just strumming the chords once and letting them ring out, or simplifying the strumming pattern.

Stage 1
Stage 2
Stage 3
Stage 4
Stage 5
Stage 6
Stage 7
Stage 8
Stage 9
Bonus

Little Talks

Words & Music by Ragnar Thorhallsson
& Nanna Bryndis Hilmarsdottir

Capo
Fret
1

♩=208

Intro

‖: Am | F | C | G :‖ *Play x4*
(Hey!)

Verse 1

Am   F   C   C
I don't like walking around this old and empty house,

    Am   F   C   C
So hold my hand, I'll walk with you, my dear.

      Am   F   C   C
The stairs creak as you sleep, it's keeping me a - wake,

      Am   F   C   C
It's the house telling you to close your eyes.

      Am   F   C   C
And some days I can't even   dress my - self,

    Am   F   C   C
It's killing me to see you this way.

              Am   F
'Cause though the truth may vary,

    C   G   Am   F   C   C
This   ship will carry our bodies safe to shore.

Link 1

As Intro

Verse 2

There's an old voice in my head that's holding me back,
Well, tell her that I miss our little talks.
Soon it will be over and buried with our past,
We used to play outside when we were young
And full of life and full of love.
Some days I don't know if I am wrong or right,
Your mind is playing tricks on you, my dear.
'Cause though the truth may vary,
This ship will carry our bodies safe to shore. (Hey.)

Chorus 1

      Am   F   C   G
Don't listen to a word I say.   (Hey!)

      Am   F   C   G
The screams all sound the same.   (Hey!)

        Am   F
Though the truth may vary,

    C   G   Am   F   C   G
This   ship will carry our bodies safe to shore.

Link 2

‖: Am | F | C | G :‖ *(Play x4)*
(Hey!)

| Am | Am | Am | Am |

Bridge

      Am *(let ring)*
You're gone, gone, gone away, I watched you disappear,
All that's left is the ghost of you.

           Am *(let ring)*
Now we're torn, torn, torn apart, there's nothing we can do,
Just let me go, we'll meet again soon.

© COPYRIGHT 2011 SONY/ATV SONGS LLC
SONY/ATV MUSIC PUBLISHING
ALL RIGHTS RESERVED. INTERNATIONAL COPYRIGHT SECURED.

cont.

      Am   F   C   C
Now wait, wait, wait for me,   please hang a - round,

      Am   F   C   N.C.
I'll see you when I fall a - sleep. (Hey!)

Chorus 2   As Chorus 1 (*Play x2*)

Outro

     (G)   **Am**   **F**
Though the truth may vary,

        C   G   Am   F   C   C
This   ship will carry our bodies safe to shore.
Though the truth may vary,
This ship will carry our bodies safe to shore.

Introduction

This folky hit was released by Icelandic band Of Monsters And Men.

Strumming

We start this song with a high-energy strumming pattern (below). Make sure your hand is moving all the time, consistently on every eighth-note beat, to really lock you into the groove. Listen closely to the recording —even though the tempo is very fast, the strumming part has quite a relaxed feel to it. Play beat 2 a little harder than the other strums.

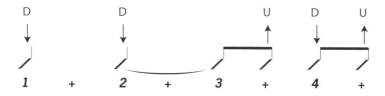

At the start of Verse 1, break down to one strum on each chord change and let it ring out. If you have a tremolo pedal then now is the time to dig it out! Halfway through the verse you can switch to playing all down-strums on the beats—this will really add to the excitement of the song.

For extra intensity, during the very last two bars of the verse you'll play even down-strums on all the eighth-notes but stop on beat 3. This is known as a 'pop stop,' and sets up the chorus, when the song will explode with energy again!

The bridge section is pretty ambient and effect-driven—I'd recommend keeping in time but again, building up the strumming slowly or (if possible) kicking in some heavy reverb, or other crazy effects!

Stage 1

Stage 2

Stage 3

Stage 4

Stage 5

Stage 6

Stage 7

Stage 8

Stage 9

Bonus

Moonlight Shadow

Words & Music by Mike Oldfield

Capo Fret 4

♩=128

Intro

| C | G | Am F | G |

Verse 1

Am   F
The last that ever she saw him,
G |C   G
Carried away by a moonlight shadow,
  |Am   F
He passed on worried and warning,
G |C   G |
Carried away by a moonlight shadow.

Pre-chorus 1

C   G
Lost in a riddle last Saturday night
|Am   F |G |
Far a - way on the other side.
              C   G
He was caught in the middle of a desperate fight,
          |Am   F |G
And she couldn't find how to push through.

Verse 2

The trees that whisper in the evening,
Carried away by a moonlight shadow,
Sing a song of sorrow and grieving,
Carried away by a moonlight shadow.

Pre-chorus 2

All she saw was a silhouette of a gun,
Far away on the other side,
He was shot six times by a man on the run,
And she couldn't find how to push through.

Chorus 1

|G C G |G C G |
   I   stay,   I   pray, see
|C   F |G
You in heaven far away.
|G C G |G C G |
   I   stay,   I   pray, see
|C   F |G
You in heaven   one day.

Verse 3

Four a.m. in the morning,
Carried away by a moonlight shadow,
I watched your vision forming,
Carried away by a moonlight shadow.

Pre-chorus 3

Star was light in a silvery night,
Far away on the other side,
Will you come to talk to me this night,
But she couldn't find how to push through.

Chorus 2

As Chorus 1

© COPYRIGHT 1983 OLDFIELD MUSIC LIMITED/STAGE THREE MUSIC (CATALOGUES) LIMITED.
STAGE THREE MUSIC PUBLISHING LIMITED, A BMG CHRYSALIS CATALOGUE.
ALL RIGHTS RESERVED. INTERNATIONAL COPYRIGHT SECURED.

Stage 1 · Stage 2 · Stage 3 · Stage 4 · Stage 5 · Stage 6 · Stage 7 · Stage 8 · Stage 9 · Bonus

justinguitar.com

Stage 1
Stage 2
Stage 3
Stage 4
Stage 5
Stage 6
Stage 7
Stage 8
Stage 9
Bonus

Verse 4	(Clean) electric guitar solo
Pre-chorus 4	Continue guitar solo (Vocals: *Far away on the other side...*)
Verse 5	(Distorted) electric guitar solo
Pre-chorus 5	Caught in the middle of a hundred-and-five. *(guitar lick)* The night was heavy and the air was alive, But she couldn't find how to push through.
Chorus 3	...Carried away by a moonlight shadow (*Repeat to fade*)

 ## Introduction

This Mike Oldfield hit, released in 1983, is a surefire classic.

Verse strumming

The strumming for this song is fairly rudimentary: consistent eighth-note strums with accents on beats 2 and 4. The 'time feel' is really nice so playing along with the recording and trying to fit right into the groove is well worth doing. You'll find that playing along with recordings will really help your feel (the way you 'sit' in the rhythm).

Chorus strumming

The chorus has some interesting things going on, starting with a double-strum before beat 1. The '+' after beat 4 would normally take an up-strum but here you play it as a down, followed by a quick up-strum, and down again on beat 1. This change of strumming speed can be tricky at first but it's a great technique to learn. Watch out for the fast chord change on beat 2 as well—to play that G to C change quickly you'll want to use the first G chord grip that we learnt on page 53.

(Pick-up)   Chorus

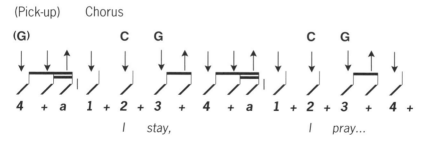

Need You Now

Words & Music by Josh Kear, Hillary Scott,
David Haywood & Charles Kelley

Capo Fret **4**

♩=108

Intro

‖: Fadd⁹ | Fadd⁹ | Am⁷ | Am⁷ :‖ *(Play x4)*

Verse 1

Fadd⁹   Fadd⁹   Am⁷   Am⁷
Picture perfect memories scattered all around the floor,
Fadd⁹   Fadd⁹   Am⁷   Am⁷
Reaching for the phone 'cause I can't fight it any - more.
     Fadd⁹   Fadd⁹   Am⁷   Am⁷
And I wonder if I ever cross your mind,
       Fadd⁹ | Fadd⁹   N.C. |
For me it happens all the time.   (It's a...)

Chorus 1

     C   C   Em⁷   Em⁷
It's a quarter after one, I'm all alone and I need you now.
   C   C   Em⁷   Em⁷
Said I wouldn't call, but I lost all control and I need you now.
     F   F   F   (Fadd⁹)
And I don't know how I can do without, I just need you now.

Link

| Fadd⁹ | Fadd⁹ | Am⁷ | Am⁷ |

Verse 2

Another shot of whiskey, can't stop looking at the door,
Wishing you'd come sweeping in the way you did before.
And I wonder if I ever cross your mind,
For me it happens all the time.

Chorus 2

As Chorus 1

Instrumental

| Am   G | C | F | G |

| Am   G | C | F | G |

Bridge

(G)   Fadd⁹   Fadd⁹   Am⁷   G
Yes, I'd rather hurt than feel nothing at all.

Chorus 3

It's a quarter after one, I'm all alone and I need you now.
And I said I wouldn't call, but I'm a little drunk and I need you now.
     Fadd⁹   Fadd⁹   Fadd⁹   C   C
And I don't know how I can do without, I just need you now.
Em⁷   Em⁷   C   C   Em⁷   Em⁷   C   C
     I just need you now.
Em⁷   Em⁷   C   C   Em⁷   Em⁷
     Oh baby, I need you now.

Outro

‖: C | C | Em | Em :‖ *(Repeat to fade)*

© COPYRIGHT 2009 WARNER TAMERLANE PUBLISHING CORPORATION/DWHAYWOOD MUSIC/
RADIOBULLETSPUBLISHING/HILLARY DAWN SONGS/EMI FORAY MUSIC/YEAR OF THE DOG MUSIC.
EMI MUSIC PUBLISHING LIMITED/WARNER/CHAPPELL NORTH AMERICA LIMITED./INTERNATIONAL DOG MUSIC.
ALL RIGHTS RESERVED. INTERNATIONAL COPYRIGHT SECURED.

Stage 1   Stage 2   Stage 3   Stage 4   Stage 5   Stage 6   Stage 7   Stage 8   Stage 9   Bonus

Stage 1
Stage 2
Stage 3
Stage 4
Stage 5
Stage 6
Stage 7
Stage 8
Stage 9
Bonus

 Introduction

This fantastic country-pop hit from Lady Antebellum is easy to play, although there are some tasty little chord extensions in there to sweeten the mix!

Rhythm

You'll probably use a similar groove throughout the song—even eighth-note down strums. You're not limited to this, but for playing high-intensity pop music, it works really well. The trick is to play just the thicker strings of any given chord—but then push through and play the whole chord on beats 2 and 4. But do try out any other patterns you like—'Old Faithful' works great for this song too!

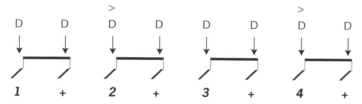

Chords

In the verse you'll see the chords Fadd9 and Am7. You can simplify these to Fmaj7 and Am if you want, although neither chord is very tricky. Just watch out on the Fadd9 that you don't play the thickest two strings.

In the chorus you'll also see an Em7, although I'd use this chord sparingly. Also watch out for the stops where the chords just ring out. I often write these as 'N.C.' which means 'No Chord', but really it's just the last chord ringing out over a pause—usually at the start or end of a chorus.

Listen out for the rhythm in the instrumental section—after the Am, the G and the C chords come on the off beats, the '+' after 3 and the '+' after 4.

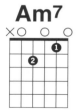
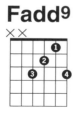
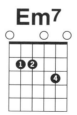

That's Entertainment
Words & Music by Paul Weller

Capo Fret **3**

♩=143

Intro

| G | Em⁷ | G | Em⁷ |
| Am⁷ | Fmaj⁷ | G | Em⁷ |

Verse 1

G   Em⁷
A police car and a screaming siren,
G   Em⁷
Pneumatic drill and ripped up concrete.
G   Em⁷
A baby wailing, stray dog howling,
G   Em⁷
A screech of brakes, a lamp light blinking.
Am⁷   Fmaj⁷   Am⁷   Fmaj⁷
That's entertainment, that's entertainment.

Link 1

| G | Em⁷ |

Verse 2

A smash of glass and the rumble of boots,
An electric train and a ripped-up phone booth.
Paint-splattered walls and the cry of a tom cat,
Lights going out and a kick in the balls, I say:
That's entertainment, that's entertainment.

Link 2

G Em⁷   G Em⁷
Ah, la la la la la, ah, la la la la la.

Verse 3

Days of speed and slow time Mondays,
Pissing down with rain on a boring Wednesday.
Watching the news and not eating your tea,
A freezing cold flat and damp on the walls, I say:
That's entertainment, that's entertainment.

Link 3

| G | Em⁷ |

Verse 4

Waking up at six a.m. on a cool warm morning,
Opening the windows and breathing in petrol.
An amateur band rehearsing in a nearby yeard,
Watching the telly and thinking about your holidays.
That's entertainment, that's entertainment.

Link 3

          (x3)
‖: G Em⁷ :‖ Am⁷ Fmaj⁷   G   Em⁷
Ah, la la la la la   ah, la la la la la

Verse 5

Waking up from bad dreams and smoking cigarettes.
Cuddling a warm girl and smelling stale perfume.
A hot summer's day and sticky black tarmac,
Feeding ducks in the park and wishing you were far away.
That's entertainment, that's entertainment.

Verse 6

Two lovers kissing amongst the screams of midnight,
Two lovers missing the tranquility of solitude.

G
○○

Em⁷
○   ○

Am⁷
✕○ ○ ○

© COPYRIGHT 1980 STYLIST MUSIC LIMITED.
UNIVERSAL MUSIC PUBLISHING MGB LIMITED.
ALL RIGHTS RESERVED. INTERNATIONAL COPYRIGHT SECURED.

justinguitar.com

Stage 1
Stage 2
Stage 3
Stage 4
Stage 5
Stage 6
Stage 7
Stage 8
Stage 9
Bonus

cont.

Getting a cab and travelling on buses,
Reading the graffiti about slashed seat affairs, I say:
That's entertainment, that's entertainment.

Outro

‖: G   Em7   *(x3)* :‖   Am7 Fmaj7
   Ah,   la la la la la   ah,   la la la la la   *(Repeat to fade)*

Introduction

This awesome song, written by Paul Weller and recorded by The Jam was originally played using barre chords, but using a capo on fret 3 gets almost exactly the same sound and is a lot easier to play!

Double-time push

The grips for the G, Em7 and Am7 chords aren't new, but I've included them anyway on the song sheet. The original recording uses an F barre, but you can substitute it with Fmaj7.

Let's start simply, with a nice stress-free strumming pattern.

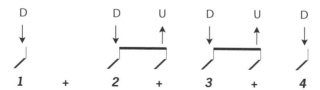

Once you've got used to the chord changes, we can tackle the double-time push. Look at the end of the strumming pattern shown below, at beat '4+' in the second bar. It's a down-strum, but all the other '+' beats use up-strums! This is the 'double-time push'!

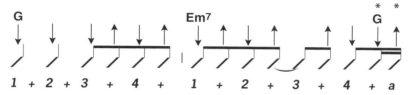

Play through the pattern very slowly, counting along out loud. Tap your foot on the numbered beats (1,2,3,4). Remember that the last two strums are twice as fast as the other strums. Take it slowly and carefully, making sure that you keep the beat consistent. Listen to the original recording to figure out where to place the double-strums, because they don't all occur at the end of the bar.

Wake Me Up

Words & Music by Aloe Blacc, Tim Bergling & Michael Einziger

Stage 1 | Stage 2 | Stage 3 | Stage 4 | Stage 5 | Stage 6 | Stage 7 | Stage 8 | Stage 9 | Bonus

♩=124

Intro

| Am   F | C/G   G | Am   F | C/G   E |

Verse 1

| Am   F | C/G
Feeling my way through the darkness,
| Am   F | C/G
Guided by a beating heart.
| Am   F | C/G
I can't tell where the journey will end,
| Am   F | C/G
But I know where to start.

C/G

Verse 2

They tell me I'm too young to understand,
They say I'm caught up in a dream.
Well, life will pass me by if I don't open up my eyes,
Well, that's fine by me.

Chorus 1

              | Am   F | C/G
So wake me up when it's all over,
G | Am F | C/G
When I'm wiser and I'm older.
E | Am   F | C/G
All this time I was finding my - self
        G | Am   F | C/G
And I   didn't know I was lost.
        E | Am   F | C/G
So wake me up when it's all over,
G | Am F | C/G
When I'm wiser and I'm older.
E | Am   F | C/G
All this time I was finding my - self
        G | Am   F | C/G
And I   didn't know I was lost.

                                      (2° N.C.)

Link

‖: Am   F | C/G   G | Am   F | C/G   E :‖

‖: Am   F | C/G   G | Am   F | C/G   E :‖ (Play x4)

Verse 3

I tried carrying the weight of the world, but I only have two hands.
Hope I get the chance to travel the world, but I don't have any plans.

Verse 4

Wish that I could stay forever this young, not afraid to close my eyes.
Life's a game made for everyone, and love is the prize.

Chorus 2

As Chorus 1

(E) ‖: Am   F | C/G   G | Am   F | C/G   E :‖
          I didn't know I was lost,   I didn't know I was lost.

Outro

‖: Am   F | C/G   G |

| Am   F | C/G   E   :‖ Play x6   (Am)

© COPYRIGHT 2013 UNIVERSAL MUSIC CORPORATION/EMI MUSIC PUBLISHING SCANDINAVIA AB/
ELEMENTARY PARTICLE MUSIC/ALOE BLACC PUBLISHING INC.
UNIVERSAL MUSIC PUBLISHING LIMITED/EMI MUSIC PUBLISHING LIMITED/UNIVERSAL/MCA MUSIC LIMITED.
ALL RIGHTS RESERVED. INTERNATIONAL COPYRIGHT SECURED.

Stage 1
Stage 2
Stage 3
Stage 4
Stage 5
Stage 6
Stage 7
Stage 8
Stage 9
Bonus

Introduction

This massive dance hit for Avicii includes a cool folky guitar part, which is pretty rare for a dance anthem. Personally I love genre blends!

Easy strumming & counting

The chords are not difficult and should be familiar, although some of the changes can be a bit tricky when played at full speed. I recommend focusing on the strumming pattern below, before you go any further. It is the 'correct' pattern but I've written it at half speed, so you can familiarise yourself with it. You may want to speed up your metronome to compensate.

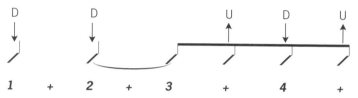

Here's the pattern again, written at the proper speed (reset your metronome to 124bpm).

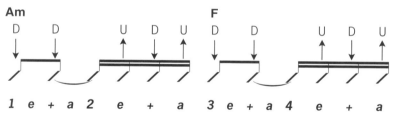

In the intro, the G and the E chords come on beat 4—not halfway through the bar as you might expect. For those chords you'll change the pattern a bit, as shown below. You'll repeat this pattern in the chorus.

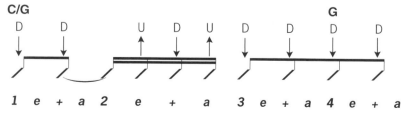

For the full-on 'house' sections of the song, you can continue to strum along or rip out a solo—you could use either the A Minor Pentatonic (BC-176) or the C Major scale. Have some fun with it!

Stage 1
Stage 2
Stage 3
Stage 4
Stage 5
Stage 6
Stage 7
Stage 8
Stage 9
Bonus

Introduction

In this stage we have some really interesting chord types—power chords (BC-172)—which are a great introduction to barre chords (which are explained in full in the *Intermediate Method*) and are used in many rock and pop songs. They are pretty easy to play and will help you remember the notes on the thickest string (see opposite). We focus on chords with a sixth-string root in Stage 7 and with a fifth-string root in Stage 8 (page 170), but when playing a song you can mix up the fifth- and sixth-string roots as you like.

Power chords are very useful: sometimes you will find a song where you know all the chords except one or two, which can be kind of annoying! For example, a song might look easy, except that you see Bm (B minor) in the chord progression, which you haven't learnt yet. Grrrr! But there is a trick: any major or minor chord can be substituted for a power chord, because power chords are neither major no minor. So rather than worry about not playing the Bm, just play a B power chord (B5) instead, and then you can play the tune. Then later on, when you've learnt how to play Bm (as a barre chord) you can revisit the song and add that chord in.

We also learn about using suspended (sus) chords (BC-173), which will really add interest to your rhythm playing once you've mastered them. It's important to practise using them in context, but also as a separate exercise, so practise these as part of your One-Minute Changes (BC-174) and then work them into your songs. You can of course use them in the songs shown in this stage, but you can also add them into other songs too, so a great exercise would be to go back through the songs from the earlier stages and try to incorporate these new sus chords. Experiment, and listen, and try to work out where they might sound effective. Do they sound better in a fast-moving chord sequence, or in a sequence where the chords change more slowly? Don't be scared to make a mistake: you will soon develop a feel for when they work and when they don't!

Strumming BC-175

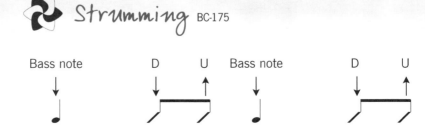

| Bass note | | D | U | Bass note | | D | U |
| 1 | + | 2 | + | 3 | + | 4 | + |

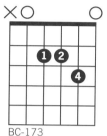

Stage 7 Chords

Asus⁴
X O   O
BC-173

Asus²
X O   O O
BC-173

Dsus⁴
X X O
BC-173

Dsus²
X X O   O
BC-173

Esus⁴
O   O O
BC-173

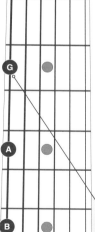

E A D G B E

F

G

A

B

C

D

E

Power Chords BC-172

The diagram on the left shows the guitar neck and the names of the natural notes on the thickest (E) string. You should memorise this so that you can find any power chord shape with its root on this string. For instance, G5 can be found at the 3rd fret.

G5
X X X

Stage 1
Stage 2
Stage 3
Stage 4
Stage 5
Stage 6
Stage 7
Stage 8
Stage 9
Bonus

Celebrity Skin

Words & Music by Billy Corgan, Courtney Love & Eric Erlandson

Stage 1
Stage 2
Stage 3
Stage 4
Stage 5
Stage 6
Stage 7
Stage 8
Stage 9
Bonus

♩=135

Verse 1

riff ⎯⎯⎯⎯⎯⎯⎯

|A⁵ C♯5 |F♯5

                   riff

Oh, make me over   I'm all I wanna be,

riff   **riff**

  A walking study   in demonology.

Chorus 1

D⁵   A⁵

Hey, so glad you could make it

D⁵   A⁵

Yeah, now you really made it

F♯5   A⁵|B⁵   C⁵ C♯5|D⁵   D⁵

Hey,   so glad you could make it   now.

Verse 2

Oh, look at my face, my name is Might Have Been
My name is Never Was, my name's Forgotten.

Chorus 2

Hey, so glad you could make it,
Yeah, now you really made it
Hey, there's only us left now.

Bridge 1

|A   D |A   D |

  When I wake up in my makeup

|A   D |F♯5

  It's too early for that dress.

|A   D |A   D |

  Wilted and faded   somewhere in Hollywood

|A   D |F♯5

  I'm glad I came here with your pound of flesh.

|A   D |A   D |

  No second billing, 'cause you're a star now

|A   D |F♯5

  Oh, Cinde - rella, they aren't sluts like you.

|A   D |A   D |

  Beautiful garbage, beautiful dresses

|A   D |F♯5   **(riff)**

  Can you stand up or will you just fall down?

Verse 3

You better watch out what you wish for
It better be worth it so much to die for.

Chorus 3

As Chorus 2

Bridge 2

When I wake up in my makeup
Have you ever felt so used up as this?
It's all so sugarless: hooker, waitress,
Model, actress, oh, just go nameless.
Honeysuckle, she's full of poison
She obliterated everything she kissed.
Now she's fading somewhere in Hollywood
I'm glad I came here with your pound of flesh.

© COPYRIGHT 1998 MOTHER MAY I MUSIC, USA/ECHO ECHO TUNES.
KOBALT MUSIC PUBLISHING LIMITED/ UNIVERSAL MUSIC PUBLISHING LIMITED.
ALL RIGHTS RESERVED. INTERNATIONAL COPYRIGHT SECURED.

Stage 1
Stage 2
Stage 3
Stage 4
Stage 5
Stage 6
Stage 7
Stage 8
Stage 9
Bonus

Verse 4 You want a part of me, well, I'm not selling cheap,
No, I'm not selling cheap.

 ## Introduction

This Hole song is a great power chord workout!

 ## Riff

The first thing to nail down is the riff—all three power chords are best played with the root on string 6, which should almost automatically create a slide down to the F#5. Make sure you nail the rhythm and keep the chords tight, meaning that they don't ring out longer than they should. Be advised that all strums throughout this song are **down-strums**.

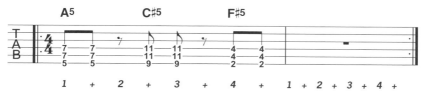

The chorus has a specific rhythm—though it's hard to hear clearly on the recording. It's a 2-bar pattern and there are variations of it throughout the song. The chord in bar 2 is 'pushed', shown below at *.

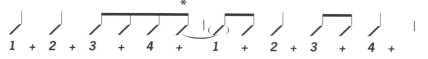

Here's the end of the chorus, which uses some nice linking chords, and a final rock-y accent pattern on the D5 chord.

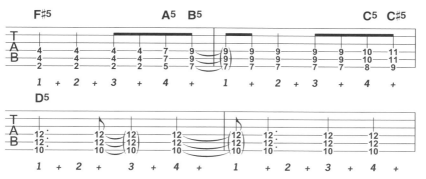

The bridge switches to a clean electric guitar sound and uses even eighth-note strumming with accents on beats 2 and 4.

149

Stage 1
Stage 2
Stage 3
Stage 4
Stage 5
Stage 6
Stage 7
Stage 8
Stage 9
Bonus

Come As You Are

Words & Music by Kurt Cobain

♩=120

Intro

riff
‖: (F♯m) | (E5) :‖ *(Play x4)*

Verse 1

riff 1 (x4)
Come as you are, as you were
As I want you to be
As a friend, as a friend
As an old enemy.

Verse 2

riff 1 (x4)
Take your time, hurry up
Choice is yours, don't be late
Take a rest as a friend
As an old memory.

F♯sus4

Chorus 1

          F♯sus4   A   F♯sus4   A
(Memor - y)   - a, (Memor - y)   - a
          F♯sus4   A   F♯sus4   A
Memor - y   - a, (Memor - y)   - a

Verse 3

Come doused in mud, soaked in bleach
As I want you to be,
As a trend, as a friend
As an old memory.

Bsus4

Chorus 2

As Chorus 1

Bridge

Bsus4 **Dsus2**   **Bsus4**   **Dsus2**
  When I swear that I don't have a gun,

   Bsus4   **Dsus2**
No I don't have a gun,

   Bsus4   **Dsus2**
No I don't have a gun.

Link

Play **riff** *(x4)*

Dsus2

Verse 4
Guitar solo
Verse 5
Guitar solo

Chorus 3

As Chorus 1

Bridge 2

As Bridge 1
...No I don't have a gun, no I don't have a gun.

Outro

Play **riff** *(x4)*

F♯sus4

© COPYRIGHT 1991 THE END OF MUSIC LLC/BMG RIGHTS MANAGEMENT (UK) LIMITED (PRIMARY WAVE).
BMG VM MUSIC LIMITED (US).
ALL RIGHTS RESERVED. INTERNATIONAL COPYRIGHT SECURED

Introduction

This awesome Nirvana song pushes the 'beginner' remit of this book a little but is well worth putting the extra practice in.

# Tuning

We're looking at the *Nevermind* recording, for which you'll need to tune your guitar down a whole tone (strings from thick to thin: DGCFAD) although the *MTV Unplugged In New York* version is detuned a semitone (from thick to thin: E♭A♭D♭G♭B♭E♭). While you're getting started you may want to work in standard tuning, and you can even use software like *Transcribe!* to tune up either of those recordings.

Riff

The main riff shown in TAB below is an all-time classic and relatively easy to play. Just use finger 1 to play notes in fret 1 and finger 2 for notes in fret 2. Try to let all the notes ring out as much as possible. For for the authentic sound you'll need a chorus effect (Kurt used an Electro-Harmonix Small Clone, set to about 9 o'clock).

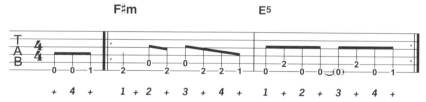

Chorus, bridge and solo

The chorus can be played using simple power chords but the actual chords are an F#sus4, and a simple open A, using a mini barre. The strumming in the chorus is 'Old Faithful' (see page 19).

The bridge can be played using power chords (again the recommended route for beginners) but you can also use the cool Bsus4 to Dsus2 as per the record, again using 'Old Faithful', perhaps developing the pattern.

The solo is easy—try to work it out yourself! All the notes are on string 3, using frets 6, 9 and 11 mostly, with one adventure up to the 13th fret.

Crazy Little Thing Called Love

Words & Music by Freddie Mercury

♩=154

Intro

‖: D Dsus4 D | D Dsus4 D :‖

Verse 1

| D Dsus4 D | D Dsus4 D |
This thing called love,

G | C G |
I just can't handle it.

| D Dsus4 D | D Dsus4 D |
This thing, called love,

G | C G |
I must get 'round to it.

D
I ain't ready.

| B♭5 C | D | D N.C. |
Crazy little thing called love.

Verse 2

This thing (this thing) called love (called love)
It cries (like a baby) in a cradle all night.
It swings, (woo–hoo) it jives, (woo–hoo)
It shakes all over like a jellyfish.
I kinda like it, crazy little thing called love.

Bridge

G G C G
There goes my baby, she knows how to rock and roll.

B♭5 B♭5 | E A
She drives me crazy, she gives me hot and cold fever,

| F N.C. |
Then she leaves me in a cold, cold (sweat.)

| (D) (C♯) (C) | (A) (G♯) (G) | E | A |
...sweat.

Verse 3

I gotta be cool relax,
Get hip, get on my tracks,
Take the back seat, hitch-hike,
And take a long ride on my motorbike
Until I'm ready, crazy little thing called love.

Guitar solo

B♭5	B♭5	D G	D
B♭5	B♭5	E A	F N.C.
(D) (C♯) (C)	(A) (G♯) (G)	E	A N.C.

Verse 4

As Verse 3 *(a capella)*

Verse 5

As Verse 1

Outro

| B♭5 C | D
‖: Crazy little thing called love. :‖ *(Repeat to fade)*

© COPYRIGHT 1979 QUEEN MUSIC LIMITED.
EMI MUSIC PUBLISHING LIMITED.
ALL RIGHTS RESERVED. INTERNATIONAL COPYRIGHT SECURED.

Stage 1 · Stage 2 · Stage 3 · Stage 4 · Stage 5 · Stage 6 · Stage 7 · Stage 8 · Stage 9 · Bonus

Introduction

This classic Queen song is unusually beginner-friendly, luckily for us!

Strumming

The song starts with a very recognisable riff based around a D and a Dsus4 chord. I'd recommend starting with the strumming pattern below and then adding the sus chord once you have the pattern sounding smooth—it's not hard at all, but if you struggle getting the little finger on and off quickly, just slow it down and build up the speed gradually.

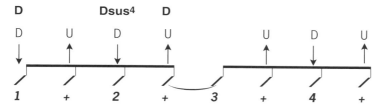

D		Dsus4	D

In the verses, stick with this strumming pattern, but when it moves from C to G, play just the down-strums on the beat, two on each chord. Listen to the recording and you can clearly hear the band picking this rhythm. The same goes for the B♭ to C chord changes. If you're a beginner you should a B♭5 then a C5 power chord, as changing to an open C chord might be tricky.

The bridge has a slightly different feel, more a kind of country swing— play the bass strings on beats 1 and 3, followed by two full strums but note that on the C chord, you should play four accented down-strums, as per the original recording.

Later in the bridge there's a fun little riff involving single notes, which appears again in the guitar solo.

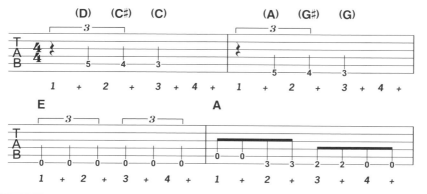

Stage 1
Stage 2
Stage 3
Stage 4
Stage 5
Stage 6
Stage 7
Stage 8
Stage 9
Bonus

Fly Away

Words & Music by Lenny Kravitz

Stage 1
Stage 2
Stage 3
Stage 4
Stage 5
Stage 6
Stage 7
Stage 8
Stage 9
Bonus

♩=160

> *Chord sequence throughout:*
>
> | A⁵ B⁵ | C⁵ | G⁵ | D⁵ | |

Intro — *(Play **riff** x4)*

Verse 1
(no guitar)

I wish that I could fly
Into the sky
So very high,
Just like a dragonfly.
I'd fly above the trees
Over the seas in all degrees,
To anywhere I please.

Chorus 1
(with riff)

Oh, I want to get away
I want to fly away,
Yeah yeah yeah.
Oh, I want to get away,
I want to fly away,
Yeah yeah yeah.

Verse 2
(with riff)

Let's go and see the stars,
The milky way or even Mars,
Where it could just be ours.
Let's fade into the sun,
Let your spirit fly,
Where we are one,
Just for a little fun,
Oh, oh, oh, yeah !

Chorus 2 — As Chorus 1

Instr.
(no guitar)

Play sequence x4

Chorus 3
(riff till end)

As Chorus 1

Chorus 4

I want to get away, *(x4)*
Yeah!
I want to get away,
I want to fly away,
Yeah, with you, girl I gotta get away!

Chorus 5 — As Chorus 4 *(vocals ad lib.)*

© COPYRIGHT 1997 MISS BESSIE MUSIC, USA.
BMG VM MUSIC LIMITED (US).
ALL RIGHTS RESERVED. INTERNATIONAL COPYRIGHT SECURED.

justinguitar.com

Stage 1
Stage 2
Stage 3
Stage 4
Stage 5
Stage 6
Stage 7
Stage 8
Stage 9
Bonus

 Introduction

This massive hit for Lenny Kravitz is based on a cool guitar riff, which anyone around in the 1990s will remember! The guitar riff comprises two slightly different parts—what I'm showing you is a combination of the two parts.

Riff

To make the music easier to read, I've written this song out in half time, which is why the metronome mark is quite fast (160bpm), even though the song isn't particularly fast at all! The count is written below the riff—all the numbered beats are played with a down-strum and the '+'s are played with an up-strum.

Your goal is to keep the chords sounding 'clean'—make sure that even if you strum all the strings, only the three notes of the power chord sound. On root 6 chords, use the underneath of finger 1 to mute all the thinner strings, and on root 5 chords press the fingertip up to mute the thickest string too. There's more info on root 5 chords in Stage 8.

Advanced players may have noticed that the riff actually uses major barre chords, so if you're familiar with them, you can use barre chords instead of power chords. There's also a Dsus4 extension, which I've added in brackets to the last bar. If you're a beginner, leave the bracketed notes out.

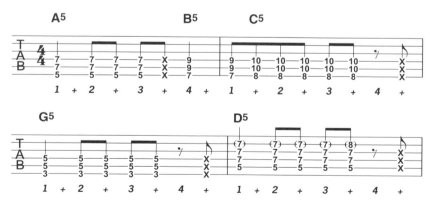

If you're playing solo, you should differentiate between the verses and choruses, either by using a clean sound for the verses and a distorted sound for the choruses or maybe heavy palm muting (BC-192) in the verse, which you remove for the chorus. On the recording the guitar is silent sometimes, but you could instead play one bass note from each chord, or copy the bass line.

Fortunate Son

Words & Music by John Fogerty

Stage 1
Stage 2
Stage 3
Stage 4
Stage 5
Stage 6
Stage 7
Stage 8
Stage 9
Bonus

♩=134

Intro

*Bass plays repeated **G** riff*

| N.C. | N.C. | ‖: (G) | (F) | (C) | (G) :‖

Verse 1

G5   F5
Some folks are born made to wave the flag
C5   G5
Ooh, they're red, white and blue
G5   F5
And when the band plays 'Hail to the chief'
C5   G5
Ooh, they point the cannon at you, Lord,

Chorus 1

G   D   C   G
It ain't me,   it ain't me,   I ain't no senator's son, son
G   D   C   G
It ain't me,   it ain't me,   I ain't no fortunate one, no.

Verse 2

Some folks are born silver spoon in hand,
Lord, don't they help themselves, oh.
But when the taxman comes to the door,
Lord, the house looks like a rummage sale, yes,

Chorus 2

It ain't me, it ain't me, I ain't no millionaire's son, no.
It ain't me, it ain't me, I ain't no fortunate one, no.

Bridge

‖: G7 | A/G | F/G | G :‖

Verse 3

Some folks inherit star-spangled eyes
Ooh, they send you down to war, Lord
And when you ask them, 'How much should we give?'
Ooh, they only answer more! more! more! yoh,

Chorus 3

It ain't me, it ain't me, I ain't no military son, son
It ain't me, it ain't me, I ain't no fortunate one, no.
It ain't me, it ain't me, I ain't no fortunate one, no, no, no,
It ain't me, it ain't me, I ain't no fortunate son, no, no, no.

© COPYRIGHT 1970 JONDORA MUSIC, USA.
PRESTIGE MUSIC LIMITED.
ALL RIGHTS RESERVED. INTERNATIONAL COPYRIGHT SECURED.

Stage 1
Stage 2
Stage 3
Stage 4
Stage 5
Stage 6
Stage 7
Stage 8
Stage 9
Bonus

Introduction

This classic Creedence Clearwater Revival track, released in 1969, was written in response to America's war in Vietnam.

Tuning / Playing the song

There are a few approaches to playing this song, largely because the guitar on the original is either tuned down a tone or is in open G tuning—it's hard to tell which. Regardless, you can play along with the record using either power chords or open chords, with the power chords being closer to the original recorded version.

The intro riff is good fun—again, I've slightly adapted the original guitar part (below). The bass guitar stays on the note G throughout this section—the chord symbols refer to the harmony outlined by the guitar.

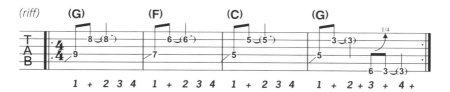

Once we kick into the verse the rhythm has a firm foundation, shown in the pattern below, although there's a fair bit of flexibility, so you'll hear extra strums in there too, which you can copy.

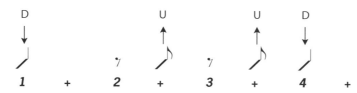

The bridge section uses some unusual chords. One guitar plays the chords as shown below and the other plays a low G as a drone, adding to the flavour! The slides are an important part of this chord riff.

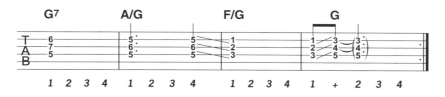

Stage 1
Stage 2
Stage 3
Stage 4
Stage 5
Stage 6
Stage 7
Stage 8
Stage 9
Bonus

Jackson

Words & Music by Jerry Leiber & Billy Edd Wheeler

♩=260

Intro

‖: C | C | C | C :‖ *(Play x4)*

Verse 1

C   C   C   C
We got married in a fever,

C   C   C   C
Hotter than a pepper sprout,

C   C   C   C
We been talkin' 'bout   Jackson

C   C   C
Ever since the fire went out,

C⁷   F   F
I'm goin' to Jackson,

F   F   C   C
  I'm goin' to mess a - round.

C   C   F   F
  Yeah, I'm goin' to Jackson,

G   G   C   C
  Look out Jackson Town.

Verse 2

Well go on down to Jackson,
Go ahead and wreck your health.
Go play your hand you big talkin' man,
And make a big blue of your self.
Yeah, go to Jackson, go comb your hair,
Honey I'm goin' to snowball Jackson, see if I care!

Verse 3

When I breeze into that city,
People gonna stoop and bow (ha!)
All them women gonna make me
Teach them what they don't know how.
Oh I'm goin' to Jackson, you turn-a loosen my coat,
'Cause I'm goin' to Jackson, 'Goodbye' that's all she wrote.

Verse 4

But they'll laugh at you in Jackson,
And I'll be dancin' on a Pony Keg.
They'll lead you 'round town like a scalded hound,
With your tail tucked between your legs,
Yeah, go to Jackson, you big-talkin' man.
And I'll be waitin' in Jackson, behind my Japan Fan.

Verse 5

Well now, we got married in a fever,
Hotter than a pepper Sprout,
We've been talkin' 'bout Jackson,
Ever since the fire went out.
I'm goin' to Jackson, and that's a fact.
Yeah, we're goin' to Jackson, ain't never comin' back.

Repeat Verse 5 to fade

© COPYRIGHT 1963 BEXHILL MUSIC CORPORATION, USA/SONY/ATV TUNES LLC.
SONY/ATV MUSIC PUBLISHING/IMAGEM MUSIC.
ALL RIGHTS RESERVED. INTERNATIONAL COPYRIGHT SECURED.

Stage 1
Stage 2
Stage 3
Stage 4
Stage 5
Stage 6
Stage 7
Stage 8
Stage 9
Bonus

Introduction

This classic song from Johnny Cash and June Carter (a hit single in 1967) is a lot of fun to play, and although the chords are very simple, you have a fast-paced rockabilly strumming pattern to keep you busy.

Strumming

Start off by listening to the chord changes—the chord sequence is essentially the same throughout the song, but occasionally the chords change a little earlier or later than expected. These subtleties will be best learnt by listening and copying, and following the lead vocal.

The classic strumming pattern for this song is the 'boom chicka' groove that Johnny Cash was a master of, and it's pretty tricky to perfect. You need to be accurate when picking your bass note, but keep your hand and arm relaxed in order to create the fast 'chick - a'. Like all guitar techniques, you'll have to practise it until it becomes instinctive.

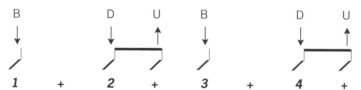

You can of course use simpler strumming (e.g. you could leave out the up-strums), but I recommend that you always retain the bass note on beats 1 and 3 (the 'boom'), as this will help create the feel of the song.

Intro

159

Rock The Casbah

Words & Music by Mick Jones, Joe Strummer & Topper Headon

♩=128

Intro

‖: Dm | Am G | Em F | Em C :‖

Verse 1

        Am   Em
Now the king told the boogie men,

           G   Dm
You have to let that raga drop.

        Am   Em
The oil down the desert way,

          G   Dm
Has been shaken to the top.

        Am   Em
The sheikh he drove his Cadillac,

          G   Dm
He went a-cruisin' down the ville.

        Am   Em   F   F
The muezzin was a-standing.   on the radia - tor grille.

Chorus 1

        Dm   Am G |
Sha - rif don't like it,

| Em   F |Em   C
Rockin' the Casbah, rock the Casbah.

     |Dm | Am G |
Sha - rif don't like it,

| Em   F |Em   C
Rockin' the Casbah, rock the Casbah   (By...)

Verse 2

By order of the prophet, we ban that boogie sound.
Degenerate the faithful, with that crazy Casbah sound.
But the Bedouin they brought out the electric camel drum.
The local guitar picker got his guitar-picking thumb.
As soon as the Sharif had cleared the square, they began to wail.

Chorus 2   As Chorus 1

Verse 3

       Am   N.C.   Am   N.C.
Now over at the temple,   oh, they really pack 'em in.

       Am   N.C.   Am   N.C.
The in-crowd say it's cool.   to dig this chanting thing.

            F   N.C.   F   G
But as the wind changed direction,   the temple band took five.

       Am   N.C.   Am   N.C.
The crowd caught a whiff,   of that crazy Casbah jive.

Chorus 3   As Chorus 1

Verse 4

The king called up his jet fighters, he said you better earn your pay.
Drop your bombs between the minarets, down the Casbah way.
As soon as the Sharif was chauffeured outta there,
The jet pilots tuned to the cockpit radio blare.
As soon as the Sharif was outta their hair, the jet pilots wailed.

Chorus 4   Repeat Chorus to fade

© COPYRIGHT 1982 NINEDEN LIMITED.
UNIVERSAL MUSIC PUBLISHING LIMITED.
ALL RIGHTS RESERVED. INTERNATIONAL COPYRIGHT SECURED.

Stage 1
Stage 2
Stage 3
Stage 4
Stage 5
Stage 6
Stage 7
Stage 8
Stage 9
Bonus

 # Introduction

This song, recorded by The Clash, is not guitar-focused but is great to strum along to. The guitar part on the recording doesn't really work out of context, so we'll be looking at chords and strumming as usual.

 ## Strumming

Our good friend 'Old Faithful' is perfect for strumming this song, both in the verses and the chorus. The thing to watch out for is that in the chorus there are two chords to each bar, therefore the chord change will happen on the '+' after beat 2 (marked with a *). This really pushes the groove along, creating quite a different feel.

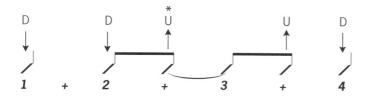

 ## Stabs

Watch out for the 'stabs' at the end of the verse on the F chord—the band all play short chords together and then build into the chorus. Play the chords as shown below and use the outside of your strumming hand to mute all the strings during the gaps. Then for the last two beats you can build up and explode into the chorus!

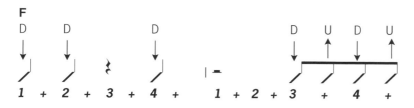

Stage 1
Stage 2
Stage 3
Stage 4
Stage 5
Stage 6
Stage 7
Stage 8
Stage 9
Bonus

T.N.T.

Words & Music by Angus Young, Malcolm Young & Bon Scott

♩=127

Intro

(let ring...)

| E5 | E5 | E5 | E5 |

Play **riff** *x4*
(Vocals 'Oi!' on offbeat)

Verse 1

Play **riff** *x7*
See me ride out of the sunset on your colour TV screen,
Out for all that I can get, if you know what I mean.
Women to the left of me, and women to the right.
Ain't got no gun, ain't got no knife,

|E   G5|A5   A5
   Don't you start no fight.

Chorus 1

(A5) |A5 G5   E5 |N.C.
'Cause I'm T.   N.   T. I'm dynamite.
|A5 G5   E5 |N.C.
T.   N.   T. and I'll win the fight.
|A5 G5   E5 |N.C.
T.   N.   T. I'm a power load.
|A5 G5   E5 |G5   A5 | (A5)
T.   N.   T.   watch me ex - plode.

E5

Link 1

Play **riff** *x2*

Verse 2

I'm dirty, mean and mighty unclean, I'm a wanted man,
Public enemy number one, understand?
So lock up your daughter, and lock up your wife
Lock up your back door and run for your life
The man is back in town,
Don't you mess me 'round.

Chorus 2

As Chorus 1

Solo

Play **riff** *x3*

|E   G5 | A5 | A5 |

Bridge

||:A5 G5   E5   :|| *Play x4*
T.   N.   T.   Oi! Oi! Oi!

Chorus 3

As Chorus 1

Outro

| E5 | F5 | F♯5 | G5 | A♭5 A5 |

| B♭5 B5 | C5 C♯5 D5 D♯5 | E5 F5 F♯5 G5 | ad lib. | E |

© COPYRIGHT 1975 J. ALBERT & SON PTY. LIMITED.
ALL RIGHTS RESERVED. INTERNATIONAL COPYRIGHT SECURED.

Justinguitar.com

Stage 1
Stage 2
Stage 3
Stage 4
Stage 5
Stage 6
Stage 7
Stage 8
Stage 9
Bonus

Introduction

Rock music doesn't get much better than AC/DC—they're what it's all about. This is one of their few songs that's suitable for beginners, although watch out at the end, when you move your power chords right up the neck of the guitar! Also, be aware that the recording is about a quarter-tone flat.

Riff

The riff starts with an open E power chord which just uses finger 1— play just the thickest 3 strings and then mute them all with the outside of your strumming hand. For the G5, put finger 2 down on fret 3 of the thickest string and lift the first finger off a bit. The underneath of finger 2 should mute string 5—strum the thickest three strings but now just strings 6 and 4 will ring out. Then put down your open A power chord and play that, then mute again. Then we have a quick succession of playing the G note (string 6 fret 3), back to the A and back to the G.

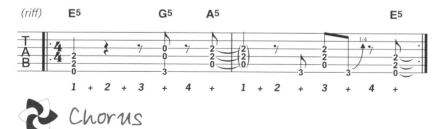

Chorus

The chorus has quite a sparse texture—the guitar only plays about half the time. If you're playing solo you might like to chug along some eighth-notes on the E bass note to fill the silence.

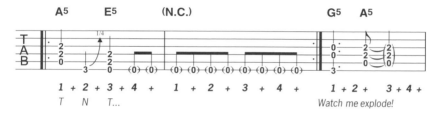

The outro is a wonderful chaos—start working your way up from the open E all the way up the neck. Listen out for the rhythm initially—at the end it's just a scramble to the top so don't worry about the chords, just make a noise!

We Are Young

Words & Music by Jeff Bhasker, Nate Ruess,
Andrew Dost & Jack Antonoff

Capo
Fret

5

♩=92

Verse 1

C   C
Give me a second I, I need to get my story straight,

 Am   Am
My friends are in the bathroom getting higher than the Empire State.

 Dm   Dm
My lover she's waiting for me just across the bar,

       F   G
My seat's been taken by some sunglasses asking 'bout a scar and

C   C
 I know I gave it to you months ago,

Am   Am
 I know you're trying to for - get.

   Dm   Dm
But be - tween the drinks and subtle things the holes in my apologies,

    F   G
You know, I'm trying hard to take it back.

   |Dm   Em |Am G F
So if by the time the bar closes and you feel like falling down,

 |F   G |
I'll carry you home. (To-)

Chorus 1

   C C Am Am   F
To - night, we are young, so let's set the world on fire,

      F   Gsus4 G
We can burn brighter than the sun.

   C C Am Am   F
To - night, we are young, so let's set the world on fire,

      F   Gsus4 G
We can burn brighter than the sun.

Verse 2

   C   C
Now, I know that I'm not all that you got,

Am
 I guess that I, I just thought,

Am   Dm
 Maybe we could find new ways to fall a - part.

        Dm
But our friends are back, so let's raise a toast,

F   G
 'Cause I found someone to carry me home.

Chorus 2

As Chorus 1

Bridge

C   F   C   G
Carry me home to - night, just carry me home to - night.

C   F   C   G
Carry me home to - night, just carry me home to - night.

C   F
 The moon is on my side, I have no reason to run,

C   G
 So will someone come and carry me home tonight.

Gsus4

X O O
① ③ ④

Stage 1 · Stage 2 · Stage 3 · Stage 4 · Stage 5 · Stage 6 · **Stage 7** · Stage 8 · Stage 9 · Bonus

164

© COPYRIGHT 2006 UNIVERSAL MUSIC PUBLISHING LIMITED/WARNER/CHAPPELL MUSIC PUBLISHING/COPYRIGHT CONTROL.
ALL RIGHTS IN GERMANY ADMINISTERED BY UNIVERSAL MUSIC PUBL. GMBH.
ALL RIGHTS RESERVED. INTERNATIONAL COPYRIGHT SECURED.

Justinguitar.com

Stage 1
Stage 2
Stage 3
Stage 4
Stage 5
Stage 6
Stage 7
Stage 8
Stage 9
Bonus

C   F
The angels never arrived,   but I can hear the choir,

C   G
So will someone come and carry me home.

Chorus 3   As Chorus 1

                 |Dm   Em |Am   G   F

Outro   So if by the time the bar closes and you feel like falling down,

       |F   G |C
I'll carry you home to - night.

 ## Introduction

Fun. are fantastic musicians, and this is their breakthrough hit from 2012.

 ## Structure and arrangement

The song uses pretty common open chords, and by focusing on the changes in dynamics (loud and soft), you get a really great song for acoustic guitar. Keep the opening section pretty sparse, just strumming the chords once, as they change. Make sure you keep time by tapping your foot—it's not 'free time' but it should feel pretty relaxed. Maintain that until the last couple of lines of Verse 1, where the tempo changes.

Once we hit the chorus, I recommend 'pumping eighth-notes', where you play all down-strums on the beats and on the '+'s, mainly strumming the thicker strings, trying to make the groove feel solid—you can emphasise this by accenting the strums on beats 2 and 4 a little.

There is a Gsus4 chord at the end which might not be familiar to you—it requires some stretching but it's not too hard. When you move to the following G chord just lift off finger 1—don't change the whole shape!

In Verse 2 the groove changes a bit, and as the original recording is pretty electronic, you have a free reign on how to interpret it. Maybe keep the eighth-notes going, add some accents or bring it back down to simple strums.

After another chorus we have the bridge. You can again interpret this how you like, as the focus is really on the lead vocal. The following pattern should fit the rhythm of the vocal well.

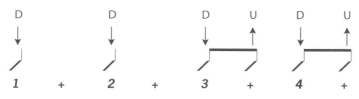

165

Stage 1
Stage 2
Stage 3
Stage 4
Stage 5
Stage 6
Stage 7
Stage 8
Stage 9
Bonus

All I Want Is You

Words & Music by U2

♩=94

Intro

| A | D | A | D |

Verse 1

     A   D   A   D
You say you want diamonds on a ring of gold,
     A   D   A   D
You say you want your story to remain un - told.

Chorus 1

                F♯m   D   F♯m   D
But all the promises we make from the cradle to the grave,
        A D   A   D
When all I want is you.

Link 1

| A(sus2) | D(sus2) | A(sus2) | D(sus2) |

Verse 2

You say you'll give me a highway with no one on it,
Treasure, just to look upon it,
All the riches in the night.

Verse 3

You say you'll give me eyes in the moon of blindness,
A river in a time of dryness,
A harbour in the tempest.

Chorus 2

As Chorus 1

Link 2

| A(sus2) | D(sus2) | A(sus2) | D(sus2) |

| A | D | A | D |

Verse 4

You say you want your love to work out right,
To last with me through the night.

Verse 5

You say you want diamonds on a ring of gold.
Your story to remain untold,
Your love not to grow cold.

Chorus 3

All the promises we break
From the cradle to the grave,
When all I want is you.

Link 3

‖: A | D :‖ *Play x5*

Outro

   A   D
‖: You,   all I want is :‖ *Play x3*

‖: A | D :‖ *Repeat to fade*

© COPYRIGHT 1988 BLUE MOUNTAIN MUSIC LIMITED (FOR THE UK)/MOTHER MUSIC (FOR THE REPUBLIC OF IRELAND)/
UNIVERSAL INTERNATIONAL MUSIC PUBLISHING B.V. (FOR THE REST OF THE WORLD).
ALL RIGHTS RESERVED. INTERNATIONAL COPYRIGHT SECURED.

Introduction

This beautiful song from U2, featured on *Rattle And Hum* (1989) is a nice little study in using your A and D sus2 chords. You'll find both chords on page 147, although if you'd rather keep things simple, you can substitute the sus chords for regular A and D chords. Be aware that guitar on the recording is tuned down a semitone (strings from low to high: E♭, A♭, D♭, G♭, B♭, E♭).

Chords

There is one gnarly chord, the F# minor, which looks like a beginner's nightmare but can be simplified by just playing the thinnest four strings. The little barre with finger 1 on the thinnest three strings is not too tricky for most beginners, but reaching over with finger 3 onto string 4 might take some practice. I really don't recommend tackling the big barre chord (below right) but it's here for any intermediate or extra ambitious beginners.

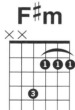

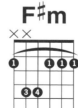

Strumming

To recreate the strumming pattern, play all eighth-note down-strums, incorporating the accents shown below. I like to use my thumb to get a fat, warm sound, playing slightly harder on the accents (>), but experiment with it, and find a version that you're happy with.

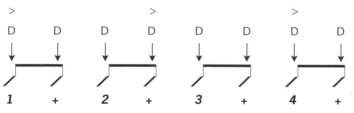

Stage 1
Stage 2
Stage 3
Stage 4
Stage 5
Stage 6
Stage 7
Stage 8
Stage 9
Bonus

Stage 1 Stage 2 Stage 3 Stage 4 Stage 5 Stage 6 Stage 7 Stage 8 Stage 9 Bonus

 Playing the riff

If you've got to know the chords Asus2 and Dsus2, the main electric guitar riff will put them to good use! The riff will take a little practice, and really requires internalising the rhythm before you can play it convincingly. Also be aware that there's a very fast delay effect on the guitar in the recording, which would be almost impossible to recreate without technology!

The main riff is two bars long and uses a mixture of down- and up-strums. I'd suggest you play it through a bunch of times very slowly and get used to how it feels and sounds and then gradually speed it up, once your left and right hands are in sync. It's just a matter of lifting one finger off to create the sus chords—this isn't difficult in theory but it may take a while to coordinate.

Riff

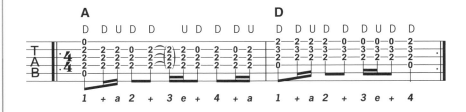

Stage 7: Final notes

Are there any songs or techniques that you want to revisit later in the course? Write them down!

Stage 1

Stage 2

Stage 3

Stage 4

Stage 5

Stage 6

Stage 7

Stage 8

Stage 9

Bonus

Stage 1

Stage 2

Stage 3

Stage 4

Stage 5

Stage 6

Stage 7

Stage 8

Stage 9

Bonus

STAGE 8 BC-181—BC-189

C5

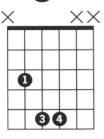

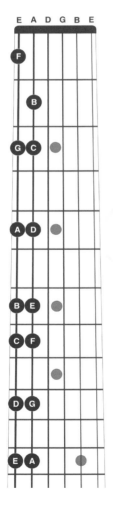

℞ Introduction

Stage 8 is your second and final lesson on power chords—once you have absorbed all the information, you should be able to play power chords using both fifth- and sixth-string root notes—go back and look at the tunes from the last stage and work out when you should use a fifth-string root and when to use a sixth-string root. This is something you have to learn: don't always expect to be shown or told which to use! The diagram on the left shows the notes on the fifth string for playing chords such as C5, also shown. We also look at a few different ways to play the G chord (BC-181). Again, you have to figure out which shape to use and when to use it. It's partly to do with minimising how far you move up and down the fretboard in between each chord, and therefore depends on the sequence of chords, and it's also about the style of music you are playing. So think, listen, and try to develop the confidence to choose your grip! Don't forget to keep practising your One-Minute Changes (BC-182).

We also look at a 12-bar blues shuffle (BC-183), so now would be a good time to go and re-visit the blues songs we covered back in Stage 5 and apply that shuffle pattern to them. The new strumming we check out is very cool: a much-used technique in many styles but most obviously folk and country. It is worth trying out on songs you have learnt earlier of course; try to get a feel for when a particular pattern is going to work. You will only develop that by trying stuff and making mistakes—don't be scared—just get in there!

We also have a couple of songs with the potential for fingerstyle arrangements (BC-184).You might find them tricky at first, but they will get better with practice and eventually seem easy. It takes a lot of practice to be able to improvise a picking pattern and sing at the same time, but it's great fun to play around with various patterns. The only important 'rule' is to make sure you play the bass note root on the beat or change of each chord.

170

Stage 8 Chords

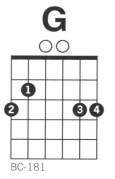

G

BC-181

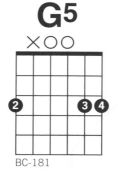

G5

BC-181

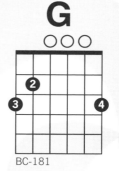

G

BC-181

Shuffle Riff BC-183

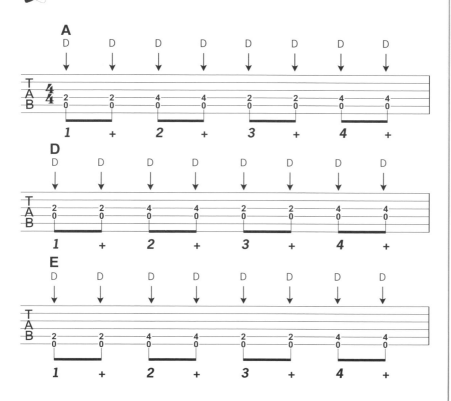

Stage 1
Stage 2
Stage 3
Stage 4
Stage 5
Stage 6
Stage 7
Stage 8
Stage 9

Hit Me With Your Best Shot

Words & Music by Eddie Schwartz

♩=128

Intro

‖: E5 A5 | C♯5 B5 | E5 A5 | C♯5 B5 A5 B5 :‖

Verse 1

       | E5   B/D♯ |C♯5   A5
You're a real tough cook - ie with the long history
      | B5   B5
Of breaking little hearts like the one in me.
| E5   B/D♯ |C♯5   A5 |
    That's ok, let's see how you do it,
B5   B5
    Put up you're dukes, let's get down to it.

Chorus 1

| E5   A5 | C♯5   B5
Hit me with your best shot!
            | E5   A5 |C♯5 B5 A5 B5 |
Why don't you hit me with your best shot,
| E5   A5 | C♯5   B5
Hit me with your best shot!
      | E5   A5 | C♯5 B5 A5 B5 |
Fire away!

Verse 2

You come on with a come on, you don't fight fair
But that's ok, see if I care!
Knock me down, it's all in vain
I'll get right back on my feet again.

Chorus 2   As Chorus 1

Guitar Solo

‖: E5 B/D♯ | C♯5 A5 | B5 | B5   :‖

‖: E5 A5 | C♯5 B5 | E5 A5 | C♯5 B5 A5 B5 :‖

Verse 3

Well you're the real tough cookie with the long history
Of breaking little hearts, like the one in me
Before I put another notch in my lipstick case
You better make sure you put me in my place.

Chorus 3

Hit me with your best shot!
Come on, hit me with your best shot!
Hit me with your best shot! Fire away!
Hit me with your best shot!
Why don't you hit me with your best shot!
Hit me with your best shot! Fire away!

Outro

‖: E5 A5 | C♯5 B5 A5 B5 :‖ *Play x3*

| E | E7 |

B/D♯

© COPYRIGHT 1979 SONY/ATV MUSIC PUBLISHING (UK) LIMITED.
ALL RIGHTS RESERVED. INTERNATIONAL COPYRIGHT SECURED.

Stage 1
Stage 2
Stage 3
Stage 4
Stage 5
Stage 6
Stage 7
Stage 8
Stage 9
Bonus

Introduction

This 80's pop hit by Pat Benatar is a great song for working on your power chords and practising your rhythm and counting skills.

Riff

The intro and chorus riff uses both regular power chords and an open A power chord. Pay attention to the count and the rhythm pattern, although it's using all down-strums, which simplifies things a little!

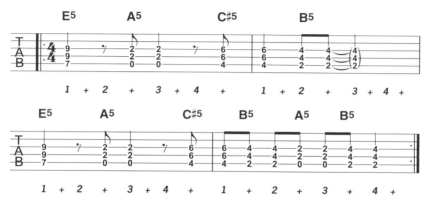

The verse introduces a chord that doesn't feature in the *Beginner's Course*—the B/D♯, which involves using a mini barre on fret 4 (see the chord diagram opposite).

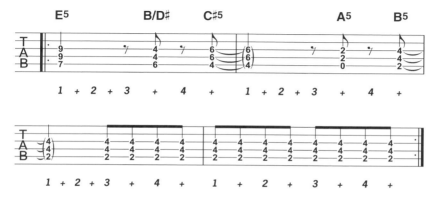

The guitar part in Verse 3 is quite complex—transcribe it if you can, otherwise simply picking out notes from the relevant chords should work!

173

Hey There Delilah

Words & Music by Tom Higgenson

♩=104

Intro
| C | Em | C | Em |

Verse 1

C   Em
Hey there Delilah, what's it like in New York City?

     C
I'm a thousand miles away, but girl,

       Em |Am Am/G |
To - night you look so pretty, yes you do.

|F   G |Am   G
Times Square can't shine as bright as you, I swear it's true.

Verse 2

Hey there Delilah, don't you worry about the distance,
I'm right there if you get lonely.
Give this song another listen, close your eyes,
Listen to my voice, it's my disguise, I'm by your side.

Chorus 1

|C   C/G |Am C/B |
Oh, it's what you do to me,
|C   C/G |Am C/B |
Oh, it's what you do to me,
|C   C/G |Am C/B
Oh, it's what you do to me,
|C   C/G |Am   C/B | C   C/G |
Oh, it's what you do to me, what you do to me.

Verse 3

Hey there Delilah, I know times are getting hard
But just believe me, girl, someday I'll pay the bills
With this guitar, we'll have it good,
We'll have the life we knew we would, my word is good.

Verse 4

Hey there Delilah, I've got so much left to say,
If every simple song I wrote to you
Would take your breath away, I'd write it all,
Even more in love with me you'd fall, we'd have it all.

Chorus 2

Oh, it's what you do to me, *(x3)*
|C   C/G |Am Am/G
Oh, it's what you do to me.

Bridge

     F
A thousand miles seems pretty far,

     G
But they've got planes and trains and cars,

   |C   C/G |Am Am/G
I'd walk to you if I had no other way.

   |F   F
Our friends would all make fun of us,

   G   G
And we'll just laugh a - long because

C/G

Am/G

C/B

© COPYRIGHT 2007 WB MUSIC CORPORATION/FEARMORE MUSIC/SO HAPPY PUBLISHING.
WARNER/CHAPPELL NORTH AMERICA LIMITED.
ALL RIGHTS RESERVED. INTERNATIONAL COPYRIGHT SECURED.

Stage 1 · Stage 2 · Stage 3 · Stage 4 · Stage 5 · Stage 6 · Stage 7 · Stage 8 · Stage 9 · Bonus

174

Stage 1

Stage 2

Stage 3

Stage 4

Stage 5

Stage 6

Stage 7

Stage 8

Stage 9

Bonus

```
       | C                                    C/B | Am      Am/G    |
       We know that none of them have felt this way.
           F           F
       De - lilah I can promise you
           G           G
       That by the time we get through
           Am                          Am
       The world will never ever be the same
               G           G
       And you're to blame.
           C                             Em
           Hey there Delilah, you be good and don't you miss me,
               C
       Two more years and you'll be done with school
           Em                         | Am      Am/G  |
       And I'll be making history like I do,
       F               G             | Am      Am/G  |
           You'll know it's all because of you,
       F               G             | Am      Am/G  |
       We can do what - ever we want     to,
       F               G             Am              G       G
           Hey there De - lilah, here's to you, this one's for you.
       || : C            C/G | Am     C/B : || C    C/G | C
           Oh, it's what you do to me.... (x8, vocals ad lib.)
```

Verse 5

Chorus 3

Introduction

This track by Plain White T's is a really satisfying song to play, and by using a capo we can eliminate the barre chords, making it much simpler.

Chords

Without the barre chords, we still have a couple more advanced chord grips. The Am/G can be a little tricky, and you have two options—my preference is to move the little finger over on to fret 3 of string 6 but if that is too much of a stretch for you, you can lift off finger 3 and use that instead of your little finger (this would technically make it Am7/G). If you really struggle, you could just stay on the Am, ignoring the G bass note.

The other two slash chords are the C/G, which is very easy—just move finger 3 on to the thickest string. Job done! The C/B is not hard either—you'll be moving from an Am, so just move finger 2 on to string 5 while leaving finger 1 down and lifting finger 3 off.

Stage 1
Stage 2
Stage 3
Stage 4
Stage 5
Stage 6
Stage 7
Stage 8
Stage 9
Bonus

Fingerstyle pattern

It's possible to strum this song, but you won't be able to recreate the feel of the original recording without using your fingers. Use your thumb to play the bass note of the chord (marked 'T'), and then play a small 'up-pluck' with finger 1, plucking from string 2 to the adjacent thicker strings. It might feel a little unusual but will just take a little practice. The trickiest aspects will probably be navigating the bass movements and getting the 'up-pluck' even and not too 'grabby'.

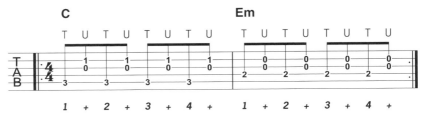

Chorus pattern

Note that in the chorus, the passing note (the C/G and C/B) only occurs on beat 4.

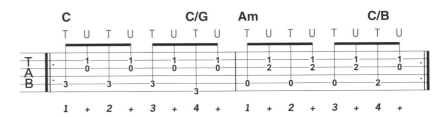

The bridge presents a new chord sequence, but nothing you haven't seen before—the chords are just slightly re-ordered.

Private Universe
Words & Music by Neil Finn

 Introduction

Crowded House's Neil Finn is one of the finest songwriters to grace this planet and this is one of my favourites of his—it's got some really interesting chords and sounds great when played solo. It's well worth seeking out some of Neil's live solo performances of the song.

Riff

You can play this song by simply strumming through the chords on the song sheet, but if you want to recreate the atmosphere of the original recording, there's quite a crucial guitar riff that you'll need to learn. The arrangement I'm using is an amalgam of the different parts you'll hear on the recording, but it should work really well, and is best suited to performing the song solo.

Make sure you keep the low A (string 5) as the lowest note, add in a little palm mute and off you go! I recommend using even eighth-note down-strums for this and really try to emulate are the accents.

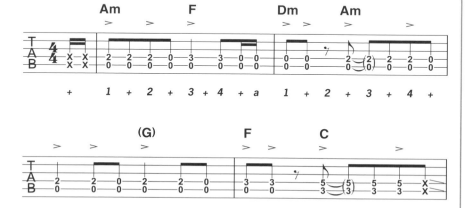

Play this riff during the intro and verse, and every time you see this sequence. Hopefully you can hear it too! After these two bars, you can just play chords, although a little palm muting will retain the character of the song.

Stage 1
Stage 2
Stage 3
Stage 4
Stage 5
Stage 6
Stage 7
Stage 8
Stage 9
Bonus

Private Universe

Words & Music by Neil Finn

♩=120

Intro

| A　F | Dm　Am | Am　　　| F　C |

Verse 1

　　Am　　　F　　　Dm　　　　Am
No time, no place to talk about the weather,
　　Am　　　G　　F　　　C
The promise of love is hard to i - gnore.
Am　　　　　　F　　　　　　Dm　　　Am
　You said the chance wasn't getting any better,
Am　　　G　　F　　　C
Labour of love is ours to en - dure.
　　Am　F　　　　　Dm　Am
The highest branch on the apple tree,
　Am　　G　　　F　　　C
It was my favourite place to be.
Am　F　　　　Dm　　　Am
I could hear them breaking free,
Am　　　G　　　F　C
But they could not see me.

Chorus 1

F　　　　G
　I will run for shelter,
C　　　　　　　Am
Endless summer, lift the curse.
F　　　　G
　It feels like nothing matters
C　　　　　　Am
In our private universe.

Link 1

| Am | Am | Am　F | Dm　Am | Am　G | F　C |

Verse 2

I have all I want, is that simple enough?
There's a whole lot more I'm thinking of.
Every night about six o'clock,
The birds come back to the palm to talk.
They talk to me, birds talk to me,
If I go down on my knees.

Chorus 2

As Chorus 1
F　　　　G
Feels like nothing matters
C　　　　　Am　　　Am
In our private universe.

Bridge 1

Am　　　　C　　　　　　　　D
　And it's a pleasure that I have known.
F　F　　　　　C　　　　　　D　　D
　And it's a treasure that I have gained.
F　F　　　　　F　　　　　　G　　G
　And it's a pleasure that I have known.

Link 2

‖: Am　F | Dm　Am | Am　G | F　C :‖

© COPYRIGHT 1993 ROUNDHEAD MUSIC, USA.
KOBALT MUSIC PUBLISHING LIMITED.
ALL RIGHTS RESERVED. INTERNATIONAL COPYRIGHT SECURED.

Verse 3	`|`Am F `|`Dm Am `|` Am G `|` F C `|`
	It's a tight squeeze but I won't let go,
	`|`Am F `|`Dm Am `|`Am G `|` F C `|`
	Time is on the table and the dinner's cold.

Chorus 3	As Chorus 1 *(Play x2)*
Outro	`||:` Am `:||` *Repeat and fade*

Strumming

The general strumming pattern is similar to the riff rhythm—here's a 'summarised' version of it.

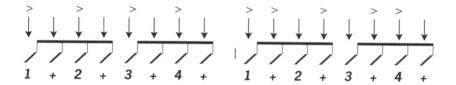

This accent pattern changes in the chorus (see below), adding a little energy to the song. The original recording consists of several overdubbed guitar parts, one just playing the chords once and letting them ring out, so feel free to experiment with the arrangement.

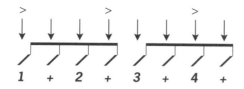

Watch out for the changes in the bridge section—some of the chord changes are not where you might expect but are nothing tricky, you just need get used to where they happen.

Stage 1
Stage 2
Stage 3
Stage 4
Stage 5
Stage 6
Stage 7
Stage 8
Stage 9
Bonus

New Slang

Words & Music by James Mercer

Stage 1

Stage 2

Stage 3

Stage 4

Stage 5

Stage 6

Stage 7

Stage 8

Stage 9

Bonus

♩=130

Vocals: 'Ooh'

Intro

| Am | Am ‖: Am C | F C | G C | Am G :‖ *(Play x4)*

| C | C |

Verse 1

Am   ²/₄ C   ⁴/₄ F   ²/₄ C   ⁴/₄ G
Gold teeth and a curse for this town, were all in my mouth.
²/₄ C   ⁴/₄ F |Am G |
Only, I don't know how they got out, dear.
Am   ²/₄ C   ⁴/₄ F ²/₄ C   ⁴/₄ G
Turn me back into the pet I was when we met.
|C   F   ²/₄ Am ⁴/₄ G   G
I was happier then with no mind-set.

Chorus 1

  G   C |F   C |G
And if you'd took to me like a   gull takes to the wind.
  G   C
Well, I'd 'a jumped from my trees
|F   C |F   C
And I'd 'a danced like the king of the eyesores
|F   C |G   G
And the rest of our lives would've fared well.

Verse 2

New slang when you notice the stripes, the dirt in your fries.
Hope it's right when you die, old and bony.
Dawn breaks like a bull through the hall,
Never should have called
But my head's to the wall and I'm lonely.

Chorus 2

And if you'd took to me like
A gull takes to the wind.
Well, I'd 'a' jumped from my tree
And I'd 'a' danced like the king of the eyesores   *1 2 3 4*
|F   C |G |G   C |
And the rest of our lives would've fared well.

Guitar solo

1 2 3 4   1 2 3 4   1 2 3 4   1 2 3 4
|F   C |F C G |C   G C |F |

1 2 3 4 1 2   1 2 3 4   1 2 3 4   1 2 3 4   1 2 3 4
|F   C ²/₄| F C ⁴/₄ |G   C |Am G | C | C |

Verse 3

Godspeed all the bakers at dawn, may they all cut their thumbs,
|C   F   ²/₄|Am ⁴/₄ G   G
And bleed into their buns 'til they melt a - way.

Chorus 3

I'm looking in on the good life I might be doomed never to find.
Without a trust or flaming fields am I too dumb to refine?
And if you'd took to me like,
I'd a danced like the queen of the eyesores,
And the rest of our lives would've fared well.

© COPYRIGHT 2007 LETTUCE FLAVORED MUSIC.
ALL RIGHTS CONTROLLED AND ADMINISTERED BY EMI MUSIC PUBLISHING LTD.
ALL RIGHTS RESERVED. INTERNATIONAL COPYRIGHT SECURED.

Outro	Am C	F C	G C	Am G	
	Am C	F C	G C	Am G	C

Stage 1
Stage 2
Stage 3
Stage 4
Stage 5
Stage 6
Stage 7
Stage 8
Stage 9
Bonus

 ## Introduction

This awesome song by The Shins is really interesting (and challenging) because of all the subtle time signature changes. They're very musical, though, and if you listen to the song a lot, they won't be hard to play, they just need to become instinctive. A useful further strategy is to read along with the music while you listen and develop a relationship between the chord chart and what you hear.

 ## Strumming

The intro fades in over the Am chord, so listen out for the tambourine (playing on beats 2 and 4) to help you get your bearings.

When strumming, play the bass string on beats 1 and 3 (just beat 1 in a bar of 2/4), following it with an up-down-up. In the intro it's particularly noticeable that the last up-strum before each chord change is the open strings ringing out while the fingers are positioning the new chord. Then we have two bars on C which is a chance to gather your composure! The 2/4 bar will be the same, just the first half of the pattern.

 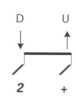 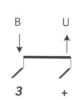 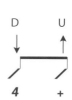

B	U	D	U	B	U	D	U
1	+	2	+	3	+	4	+

The verse has loads of changes between two- and four-beat bars, which will require close listening. After listening a lot, play simple down-strums on the beat, getting used to how the rhythm works with the melody and where the chords change.

The guitar solo has some further time signature changes and can be a bit sticky! I've written out the count above it, but again, listening and playing along with the song is the only way you'll know you've got it right!

181

Nothing Else Matters

Words & Music by James Hetfield & Lars Ulrich

Stage 1
Stage 2
Stage 3
Stage 4
Stage 5
Stage 6
Stage 7
Stage 8
Stage 9

♩.=48

Verse 1

Em | D   C |
§ So close no matter how far,
Em | D   C |
Couldn't be much more from the heart.
Em | D   C |
Forever trusting who we are,
| G   B7 | Em   Em
And nothing else matters.

Verse 2

Never opened myself this way,
Life is ours, we live it our way.
All these words I don't just say,
And nothing else matters.

Verse 3

Trust I seek and I find in you,
Every day for us something new.
Open mind for a different view,
| G   B7 | Em
And nothing else matters.

Chorus 1

| C   A | D | C   A |
Never cared for what they do,
D | C   A | D   Em   Em
Never cared for what they know,   but I know.

Verse 4

So close no matter how far,
Couldn't be much more from the heart.
Forever trusting who we are,
| G   B7 | Em
And nothing else matters.

Chorus 2

As Chorus 1

Instrumental

‖: Em | Em | Am | Am |
| C | D | Em | Em   :‖

Verse 5

As Verse 2

Verse 6

As Verse 3

Chorus 3

Never cared for what they say,
Never cared for games they play.
Never cared for what they do,
Never cared for what they know,
And I know.

Solo

| Em | D   C | Em | D   C |
| Em | D   C | G   B7 | Em | Em | Em | Em

Verse 7

As Verse 1

182

© COPYRIGHT 1991 CREEPING DEATH MUSIC.
UNIVERSAL MUSIC PUBLISHING LIMITED.
ALL RIGHTS RESERVED. INTERNATIONAL COPYRIGHT SECURED.

Justinguitar.com

Stage 1
Stage 2
Stage 3
Stage 4
Stage 5
Stage 6
Stage 7
Stage 8
Stage 9
Bonus

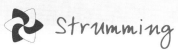 Introduction

Metal titans Metallica showed their sensitive side with this orchestral ballad on their mega-selling 'Black' album.

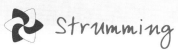 Strumming

The song is in 6/8 time, which is strummed as two groups of three. What that means in practical terms is that you will play strums 1 and 4 a little stronger than the others, so you get that feeling of ONE, two, three, FOUR, five, six, almost like a waltz. If you want to strum this song, I suggest using all down-strums on each beat to start with perhaps adding some up-strums in between if you are feeling confident.

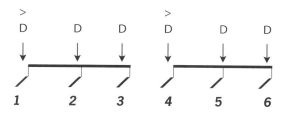

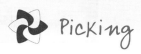 Picking

You could also try picking during the verse. You could play this kind of pattern fingerstyle, but when playing this song live James Hetfield from Metallica uses a pick, so you can try that way as well. Counting out the beats is the key to getting the rhythm right!

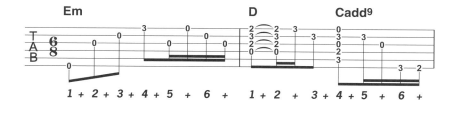

Seven Nation Army

Words & Music by Jack White

♩=125

Intro ‖: riff 1 :‖ *Play x4*

Verse 1

riff 1 (x8)
I'm gonna fight 'em off,
A seven nation army couldn't hold me back.
They're gonna rip it off,
Taking their time right behind my back.
And I'm talking to myself at night
Because I can't forget.
Back and forth through my mind
Behind a cigarette.

Pre-chorus 1

G5   A   (E5)
And the message coming from my eyes says leave it a - lone.

Chorus 1

‖: E5 G5 E5 D5 | C5   B5 | E5 G5 E5 D5 | C5 D5 C5 B5 :‖

| G5 | A | (E)

Link 1 ‖: riff 1 :‖ *Play x4*

Verse 2

Don't want to hear about it,
Every single one's got a story to tell.
Everyone knows about it,
From the Queen of England to the hounds of hell.
And if I catch it coming back my way
I'm gonna serve it to you.
And that ain't what you want to hear,
But that's what I'll do.

Pre-chorus 2 And the feeling coming from my bones says find a home.

Play x4

Chorus 2

‖: E5 G5 E5 D5 | C5   B5 | E5 G5 E5 D5 | C5 D5 C5 B5 :‖

| G5 | A | (E)

Link 2 ‖: riff 1 :‖ *Play x4*

Verse 3

I'm going to Wichita,
Far from this opera for evermore.
I'm gonna work the straw,
Make the sweat drip out of every pore.
And I'm bleeding, and I'm bleeding, and I'm bleeding
Right before the Lord.
All the words are gonna bleed from me
And I will think no more.

Pre-chorus 3 And the screams coming from my blood tell me go back home.

Chorus 3

‖: E5 G5 E5 D5 | C5   B5 | E5 G5 E5 D5 | C5 D5 C5 B5 :‖ E5

© COPYRIGHT 2002 PEPPERMINT STRIPE MUSIC, USA.
EMI MUSIC PUBLISHING LIMITED.
ALL RIGHTS RESERVED. INTERNATIONAL COPYRIGHT SECURED

Stage 1
Stage 2
Stage 3
Stage 4
Stage 5
Stage 6
Stage 7
Stage 8
Stage 9

Introduction

This massive hit brought the White Stripes to a huge audience and unleashed one of the most popular guitar riffs of all time. Make sure you copy the dramatic dynamic changes of the original recording.

Riffs

The starting riff is a bass line, played as single notes on the guitar—if you have an octave pedal, you can use that to lower the pitch, which is what Jack White did on the recording. The rhythm is vital—listen to the recording until it becomes instinctive. Use the TAB below as a guide.

(riff 1) **(E)**

The guitar explodes in on the pre-chorus, playing a bar of G5 and then A, using all down-picks and a lot of energy. Play it hard and with power but be accurate too. Make sure you only hit the necessary strings.

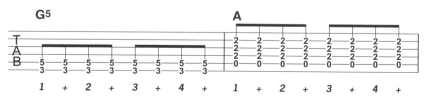

The 'chorus' guitar riff was originally played in open A tuning, but most people play it using power chords as shown below. Listen to the rhythm, count along slowly if you need to and try to get it right at a slow tempo before playing it at full speed.

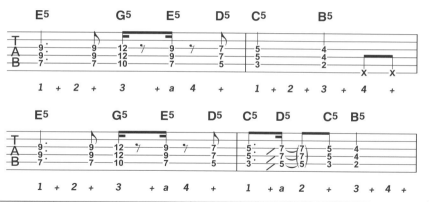

Jessie's Girl

Words & Music by Rick Springfield

Stage 1
Stage 2
Stage 3
Stage 4
Stage 5
Stage 6
Stage 7
Stage 8
Stage 9
Bonus

♩=134

Intro

riff 1
‖: D5 A5 B5 | G5 A5 D5 :‖

Verse 1

riff 1 (x4)
Jessie is a friend,
Yeah, I know he's been a good friend of mine.
But lately something's changed that ain't hard to define,
Jessie's got himself a girl and I want to make her mine.

Pre-chorus 1

riff 1 (x3)
And she's watching him with those eyes,
And she's loving him with that body, I just know it.
Yeah and he's holding her in his arms late, late at night.

Chorus 1

A5 |A5   D   A5 |B5 A5
   You know, I wish that I had Jess - ie's girl,
  B5   A5 |A5   D   A5 |B5 A5 B5 A5 |
I wish that I had Jess - ie's girl.
|G5   A5   D5 |B5   A5 |
   Where can I find a woman like that?

Verse 2

I play along with the charade,
There doesn't seem to be a reason to change.
You know, I feel so dirty when they start talking cute,
I wanna tell her that I love her but the point is prob'ly moot.

Pre-chorus 2

'Cause she's watching him with those eyes,
And she's loving him with that body, I just know it.
And he's holding her in his arms late, late at night.

Chorus 2

As Chorus 1

Chorus 3

  |A5   D   A5 |B5 A5
...like Jess - ie's girl,
  B5   A5 |A5   D   A5 |B5 A5 B5 A5 |
I wish that I had Jess - ie's girl.
|G5   A5 D5 |G5   A5 D5 |
   Where can I find a woman,
|G5   A5 D5 |B5   A5 |
   Where can I find a woman like that?

Link 1

riff 2
‖: G5 D5 | A5   :‖

Bridge

riff 2 (x4)
And I'm looking in the mirror all the time,
Wondering what she don't see in me.
I've been funny, I've been cool with the lines,
Ain't that the way love's supposed to be.

© COPYRIGHT 1980 ROBIE PORTER MUSIC.
UNIVERSAL MUSIC PUBLISHING LIMITED.
ALL RIGHTS RESERVED. INTERNATIONAL COPYRIGHT SECURED.

Stage 1
Stage 2
Stage 3
Stage 4
Stage 5
Stage 6
Stage 7
Stage 8
Stage 9
Bonus

Link 2 ‖: F#5 B5 F#5 | G#5 F#5 G#5 F#5 :‖

| G5 A5 D5 |B5 A5 |
Tell me, where can I find a woman like that?

Guitar Solo riff 1 (x4)

A5 |A5 D A5 | B5 A5

Chorus 4 You know, I wish that I had Jess - ie's girl,

B5 A5 |A5 D A5 | B5 A5 B5
I wish that I had Jess - ie's girl,

A5 |A5 D A5 | B5 A5 B5 A5 |
I want Jess - ie's girl.

|G5 A5 D5 |B5 A5 |
Where can I find a woman like that?

Chorus 5 Like Jessie's girl,
I wish that I had Jessie's girl,
I want, I want Jessie's girl.

Outro |A5 D |A5 D A5 G5 |D5 |

🌀 Introduction

This Rick Springfield classic has a cracking riff, and plenty of power chords!

🌀 Power chord riff

The most important element of the guitar part is the rhythm. Although I've written out the intro and verse riff below (labelled as **riff 1**), you really need to listen to the song and internalise the rhythm.

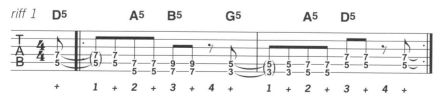

To create a more intense sound, you should palm mute (with your picking hand, see BC-192) and play **all down-strums**. Be aware that the verse riff is 'anticipated', meaning that it starts on the '+' after 4, not on beat 1!

continued... 187

Stage 1
Stage 2
Stage 3
Stage 4
Stage 5
Stage 6
Stage 7
Stage 8
Stage 9
Bonus

Chorus

During the transition from the verse into the chorus there is a 'build' on A5, and then we're into a different feel again. Here is the chorus sequence, which uses a mini-barre in the first two chord shapes, then power chords. Chorus 3 and 4 follow a slightly different structure, but the chords themselves are the same. Also, for advanced players—the B5 is in fact a Bm chord (see page 242 for the voicing), which we've simplified.

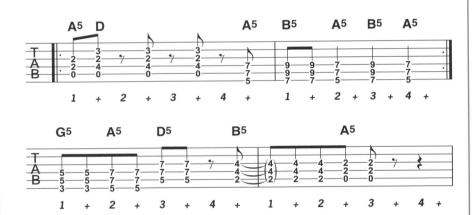

The chords for the link and bridge sections (**riff 2**) are an approximation, as the part is played by a synth, and the guitar just plays a low G note on every eighth-note. If you're playing it, the A5 chord should be anticipated. Finally, the 'Link' section follows the same rhythm as the first two bars of the chorus, except now we're using all power chords, transposed down to a different key.

Thinking Out Loud

Words & Music by Ed Sheeran & Amy Wadge

Stage 1
Stage 2
Stage 3
Stage 4
Stage 5
Stage 6
Stage 7
Stage 8
Stage 9
Bonus

Introduction

What a great songwriter Ed Sheeran is—and his performance on this recording is superb. I have a full run-through of this song on my website, but it works really well in this simplified version too.

Chords

The first thing to tackle is the D/F♯, which Ed plays by re-fretting, leaving finger 3 down from the D chord and moving fingers 1 and 2. The G is played using only fingers 2 and 3 and the A is played as a mini barre. The other tricky chord is the Bm. This is played as kind if 'half-barre' chord, which I've displayed for you. Have a go at playing it, and if you find it really hard I've written out an alternative chord (Bm7) that will work until you're ready for the proper Bm.

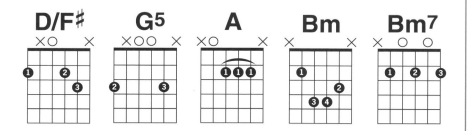

D/F♯   **G5**   **A**   **Bm**   **Bm7**

Fingerstyle

While it's possible to strum this song, it's much better suited to fingerstyle playing. There are also some nice percussive hits, which will bring another dimension to your playing. Turn over for a few examples of fingerstyle playing for this song.

Thinking Out Loud

Words & Music by Ed Sheeran & Amy Wadge

♩=80

Verse 1

|D D/F♯ |G   A |
When your legs don't work like they used to before

|D D/F♯ |G   A |
And I can't sweep you off of your feet.

|D D/F♯ |G   A |
Will your mouth still remember the taste of my love?

|D D/F♯ |G   A
Will your eyes still smile from your cheeks?

Pre-chorus 1

(A) |D D/F♯ |G A |D D/F♯ |G A
And, darling, I   will be loving you   till we're seventy.

                        |D D/F♯ |G   A |D D/F♯
And, baby, my heart could still fall   as hard at twenty three.

|G   A |Em |A   D |
      And I'm thinking 'bout how people fall in love in my - sterious ways,

Em   A
Maybe just the touch of a hand.

            Em |A   Bm
Well, me, I fall in love with you eve - ry single day

            |Em   A
And I just wanna tell you,

Chorus 1

N.C. |D D/F♯ |G
So honey now,

A |D D/F♯ |G
Take me into your loving arms,

A |D   D/F♯ |G
Kiss me under the light of a thousand stars,

A |D D/F♯ |G   A
Place your head on my beating heart.   I'm thinking out loud

                    |Bm A   G   D/F♯ |Em   A   D | D
That maybe we found love right where we are.

Verse 2

When my hair's all but gone and my memory fades
And the crowds don't remember my name.
When my hands don't play the strings the same way,
Mmm, I know you will still love me the same.

Pre-chorus 2

'Cause honey your soul could never grow old, it's evergreen,
And, baby, your smile's forever in my mind and memory.
I'm thinking 'bout how people fall in love in mysterious ways,
Maybe it's all part of a plan.
Well, I'll just keep on making the same mistakes,
Hoping that you'll understand.

Chorus 2

But, baby, now...

© COPYRIGHT 2014 SONY/ATV MUSIC PUBLISHING/BDI MUSIC LIMITED.
ALL RIGHTS RESERVED. INTERNATIONAL COPYRIGHT SECURED.

Stage 1
Stage 2
Stage 3
Stage 4
Stage 5
Stage 6
Stage 7
Stage 8
Stage 9
Bonus

justinguitar.com

Stage 1

Stage 2

Stage 3

Stage 4

Stage 5

Stage 6

Stage 7

Stage 8

Stage 9

Bonus

Instrumental ‖: D D/F♯ | G A | D D/F♯ | G A :‖

Chorus 3 So, baby, now...

Outro Oh, baby, we found love right where we are.
And we found love right where we are.

 Fingerstyle

Start with the pattern below—this is the main groove and you should get really comfortable with it before adding any embellishments:

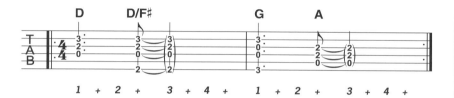

Use your fingers to pick the strings and hit all your fingers into the strings to get the percussive hit. There are a couple of optional embellishments to the guitar part, including 'hammer-ons', where you hammer down a finger without picking the note again—see the TAB below.

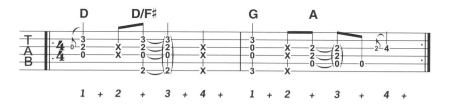

The only other slightly sticky bit is where the chords change quickly at the end of the chorus—I've written them out below with the rhythm count, as usual. Start by practising this slowly and really get comfortable with it before working up to full speed.

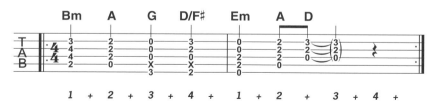

Valerie

Words & Music by Sean Payne, David McCabe, Boyan Chowdhury,
Russell Pritchard & Abigail Harding

Capo Fret **3**

♩=214

Intro ‖: C | C | C | C :‖

Verse 1

Cmaj7   Cmaj7   Cmaj7
Well, some - times I go out by myself

Cmaj7   Dm7   Dm7   Dm7   Dm7
And I look across the water.

Cmaj7   Cmaj7   Cmaj7
And I think of all the things, what you're doing

Cmaj7   Dm7   Dm7   Dm7   Dm7
And in my head I paint a picture.

Chorus 1

F   F   Em   Em
Well, since I've come-a home, well my body's been a mess,

F   F   Em   Em
And I've missed your ginger hair, and the way you like to dress.

F   F   Em   Em   G   G
 Won't you come on over,   stop making a fool out of me,

G7   G7   Cmaj7   Cmaj7   Cmaj7 Cmaj7
Why don't you come on over, Valerie?

Dm7   Dm7   Dm7   Dm7
Vale - rie.

Cmaj7   Cmaj7   Cmaj7   Cmaj7
Valerie.

Dm7   Dm7   Dm7   Dm7
Vale - rie.

Verse 2

Did you have to go to jail, put your house on up for sale,
Did you get a good lawyer?
I hope you didn't catch a tan,
I hope you find the right man who'll fix it for you.

Verse 3

And are you shopping anywhere,
Changed the colour of your hair, and are you busy?
And did you have to pay that fine
That you was dodging all the time are you still dizzy?

Chorus 2 As Chorus 1

Verse 4 As Verse 1

Chorus 3 As Chorus 1

...Valerie, Valerie, Valerie, Valerie.

Outro

(Dm7)   Cmaj7
Why don't you come on over, Vale - rie?

© COPYRIGHT 2006 EMI MUSIC PUBLISHING LTD.
ALL RIGHTS IN THE U.S. AND CANADA CONTROLLED AND ADMINISTERED BY EMI BLACKWOOD MUSIC INC.
ALL RIGHTS RESERVED. INTERNATIONAL COPYRIGHT SECURED.

Stage 1 | Stage 2 | Stage 3 | Stage 4 | Stage 5 | Stage 6 | Stage 7 | Stage 8 | Stage 9

 Introduction

Amy Winehouse was an incredible artist with some seriously special magic in her voice. This is her cover of the Zutons' song 'Valerie' (the original version is also worth catching if you don't know it).

Chords

There are many ways of approaching this song—we'll be looking at a strumming arrangement but as you progress you should revisit this song and try some other ways of performing it, maybe using riffs or 'chips' on the guitar.

There are a couple of cool chords in the song: the first is Cmaj7, which is very easy—just play a normal C chord and lift of finger 1. The Dm7 is not tricky but does require a mini barre with finger 1—you can always substitute a regular Dm if you find it tricky.

Strumming

If you're playing solo, the strumming pattern below should work well. Only play the bass strings on beat 1, all the strings of the chord on beat 2 and then UDU at the end. It also works really well on the Amy Winehouse / Mark Ronson arrangement.

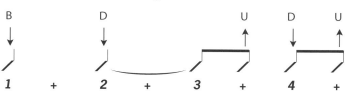

Stage 1
Stage 2
Stage 3
Stage 4
Stage 5
Stage 6
Stage 7
Stage 8
Stage 9
Bonus

We're Not Gonna Take It

Words & Music by Daniel Snider

♩=148

Intro

| |————— 4 —————| | *Drum solo*

N.C.
We're not gonna take it, no, we ain't gonna take it
|E5　D#5|C#5　B5　|　E5　D#5|C#5　B5　|
We're not gonna take it any more

Verse 1

E5　　　　　　　B5
　We've got the right to choose and
E5　　　　　　　　A5
　There ain't no way we'll lose it
E5　　　　　　　B5　　　　　　　E5　　B5
　This is our life, this is our song

Verse 2

We'll fight the powers that be just
Don't pick our destiny 'cause
You don't know us, you don't belong

Chorus 1

E5　　　　　　　B5　　　　E5　　　　　　　　　　A5
We're not gonna take it, no, we ain't gonna take it
E5　　　　　　　B5　　　　|E5　D#5|C#5　B5　|
We're not gonna take it any more

Verse 3

Oh you're so condescending
Your goal is never ending
We don't want nothin', not a thing from you

Verse 4

Your life is trite and jaded
Boring and confiscated
If that's your best, your best won't do

Bridge

D5　　　|C#5　B5　|　D5　　　|C#5　B5　|
　Woah, oh,　oh,　　　Woah, oh,　oh,
　　　　　E5　　　　　　　　F5
We're right (yeah), we're free (yeah),
　　　　F#5　　　　　　　B5　　　　　B5
We'll fight (yeah), you'll see (yeah)　 whoa,

Chorus 2

E5　　　　　　　B5　　　　E5　　　　　　　　　　A5
We're not gonna take it, no, we ain't gonna take it
E5　　　　　　　B5　　　　E5　　　B5
We're not gonna take it any more

Chorus 3

As Chorus 1

Solo

Chords as Verse 1
Chords as Chorus 1

Bridge 2

As Bridge 1

Chorus 4

As Chorus 2 (first time **N.C.** *then repeat to fade*)

© COPYRIGHT 1984 SNIDEST MUSIC COMPANY.
IMAGEM LONDON LIMITED.
ALL RIGHTS RESERVED. INTERNATIONAL COPYRIGHT SECURED.

Stage 1
Stage 2
Stage 3
Stage 4
Stage 5
Stage 6
Stage 7
Stage 8
Stage 9
Bonus

Introduction

This hilarious hit from Twisted Sister is a great tune for working on your fretted power chords and palm muting. I loved this song as a teenager but the video looks so funny now. Any of you youngsters probably wouldn't believe how people dressed in the 'hair metal' years—we actually thought it looked tough!

Power chords

The opening 2-bar sequence is also used at the end of the chorus and is just a descending power chord with a string 5 root—just watch (and listen) out for the rhythm.

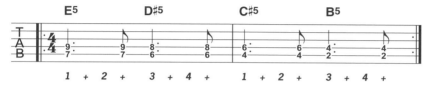

Once we're into the verse it's chugging eighth-notes—that is eight down-picks to the bar with palm muting. The only respite is on beat 1 of the last B5 power chord, where you should put a stop and then a build, quite a common trick in blues and rock music.

The chorus has a few layers weaving together and the bass adds a lot of riffing, but I'd recommend alternating between playing the chord once, letting it ring out for the whole bar, and then in the next bar chugging on all (eight) eighth-notes.

The bridge involves some very heavily muted chugging and then a rising line of power chords played on beat 1 and the '+' after 2 until the build on the B5.

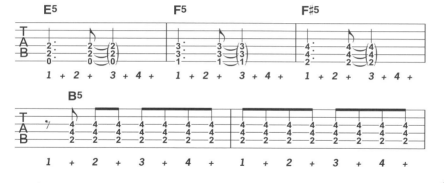

195

Stage 1
Stage 2
Stage 3
Stage 4
Stage 5
Stage 6
Stage 7
Stage 8
Stage 9
Bonus

STAGE 9 BC-191—BC-199

Introduction

We're nearly there! Hopefully you are feeling confident with it all—we have a few new things to check out in Stage 9 and then we just need to consolidate what we've learnt.

Slash chords (which have nothing to do with Guns N' Roses...) are really easy but many people get confused by their names. If you are not sure then check out my website lesson (BC-191), which will give you a full explanation.

We also have some fingerstyle patterns that you can play about with. You have a lot of flexibility when playing fingerstyle—it's a really useful technique, and one that can be employed on many songs, even if they don't feature fingerstyle playing on the original recording. Songs we looked at earlier like 'Need You Now' (page 140) will sound lovely when played fingerstyle. Fingerstyle playing sounds particularly good on folk songs and ballads. So give it a try!

If you have a jam buddy, and want to start improvising, you might like to revise the blues songs that we learnt in Stage 5. You should also try using the 12-Bar Variations (BC-194) on them too; they will sound great and if you have been listening to some blues (as instructed) then you will certainly be familiar with how they sound. Now it's time to apply them!

Stage 9: Your notes

Stage 9 Chords

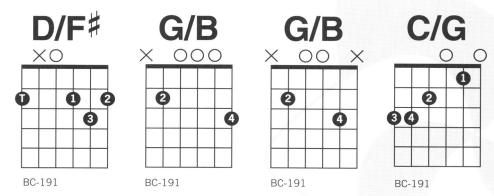

D/F♯	G/B	G/B	C/G
BC-191	BC-191	BC-191	BC-191

Applied fingerstyle Patterns BC-193

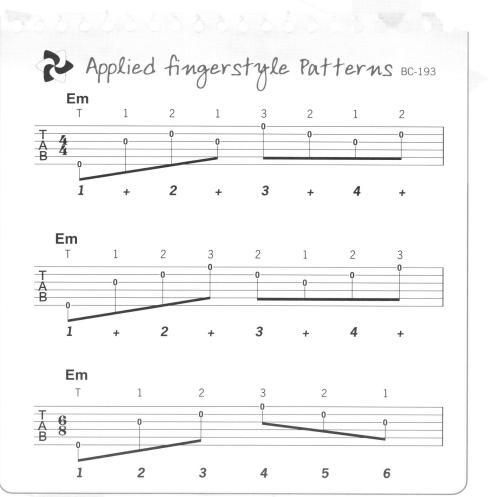

All You Need Is Love

Words & Music by John Lennon & Paul McCartney

Stage 1
Stage 2
Stage 3
Stage 4
Stage 5
Stage 6
Stage 7
Stage 8
Stage 9
Bonus

♩=100

G

Em⁷

Intro
Brass fanfare

Verse 1

```
 1  2    3   4   1   2  3
|G     D/F♯ |Em⁷    |
```
Love, love, love,

```
 1  2    3   4   1   2  3
|G     D/F♯ |Em⁷    |
```
Love, love, love,

```
 1  2   3   4  1 2  3  4
|Am    G    |D    D/E   |
```
Love, love, love.

```
 1  2   3   4   1   2  3
| D    D/C |(D)     |
```

Verse 2
There's nothing you can do that can't be done,
Nothing you can sing that can't be sung,
Nothing you can say, but you can learn how to play the game,
It's easy.

Verse 3
Nothing you can make that can't be made,
No one you can save that can't be saved,
Nothing you can do, but you can learn how to be you in time,
It's easy.

Chorus 1

```
|G         A⁷    |D     D⁷ |
```
     All you need is love,
```
|G         A⁷    |D     D⁷ |
```
     All you need is love,
```
|G         B⁷    |Em    Em⁷  |
```
     All you need is love, love,
```
|C         D⁷        ²₄|G        |
```
     Love is all you need.

Verse 4
As Verse 1 *(w/ guitar solo)*

Chorus 2
As Chorus 1

Verse 5
There's nothing you can know that isn't known,
There's nothing you can see that isn't shown,
There's nowhere you can be that isn't where you're meant to be,
It's easy.

Chorus 3
As Chorus 1 *(Play x2)*

Outro

```
G                              G
‖: Love is all you need. (Love is all you need.) :‖ Repeat to fade
```

© COPYRIGHT 1967 SONY/ATV MUSIC PUBLISHING.
ALL RIGHTS RESERVED. INTERNATIONAL COPYRIGHT SECURED.

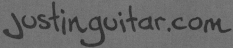

Stage 1

Stage 2

Stage 3

Stage 4

Stage 5

Stage 6

Stage 7

Stage 8

Stage 9

Bonus

 # Introduction

This Beatles classic has some really interesting things going on rhythmically. This can be tricky but it's great fun, and it's a good study in using slash chords.

Strumming & counting

There are a couple of single notes at the end of the phrase (below) (open D, then E, fret 2 of same string) that can be a little awkward. Luckily there are a couple of tricks that will help you out. The first is to keep finger 3 down in fret 3 of string 2 for the G, D/F♯ and the Em7. This will give you an 'anchor' and make the chord changes easier. The second tip is to use finger 1 for the single notes, which will free up finger 2 to get to the bass note of G on beat 1.

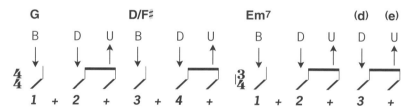

Note that we shift back to 4/4 for the third line—just use the first half of the pattern above, twice, and we use this pattern for the chorus too (though you'll use half of it for the sneaky 2/4 bar at the end).

Bass movement

There's a lovely bass movement during the third line of the verse, where we're in 4/4, starting on the Am, till the end of the verse. See below:

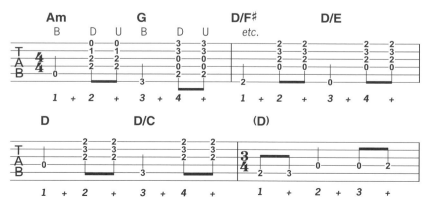

Always On My Mind

Words & Music by Mark James, Wayne Thompson & Johnny Christopher

Stage 1
Stage 2
Stage 3
Stage 4
Stage 5
Stage 6
Stage 7
Stage 8
Stage 9
Bonus

♩=90

Em7

C/B

Intro
| G | G | |

Verse 1
|G   D/F♯
  Maybe I didn't treat you,
|Em   Em7 |C   D |
  Quite as good as I should have.
|G   D/F♯
  Maybe I didn't love you,
|Em   Em7 |A7
  Quite as often as I could have.

Pre-chorus 1
C   G
  Little things I should have said and done,
|C   C/B |Am   C/G |
  I just never took the time.
|D   Em   D/F♯ |G   Am G/B |
  You were always on my mind,
|C   D |G   C D |
  You were always on my mind.

Verse 2
Maybe I didn't hold you, all those lonely, lonely times.
And I guess I never told you, I'm so happy that you're mine.

Pre-chorus 2
If I made you feel second best, girl, I'm so sorry I was blind.
You were always on my mind, you were always on my mind.

Bridge
|G   D/F♯ |Em   Em7 |
Tell   me,
|C   C/B |Am   D |
Tell me that your sweet love hasn't died.
|G   D/F♯ |Em   Em7 |
Give   me,   give me
|C   C/B |Am   D | (G)
One more chance to keep you satis - fied,   satis - fied.

Guitar solo
| G |D/F♯ | Em Em7 | A7 |

Verse 3
Little things I should have said and done, I just never took the time.
You were always on my mind,
C   D
  You were always on my mind.

Instr.
| G D/F♯ | Em Em7 | C   C/B | Am D |

N.C.   G   G
You were always on my mind...

Verse 4 As Verse 1
Verse 5 As Verse 2
Verse 6 As Verse 1 *(to fade)*

© COPYRIGHT 1971 (RENEWED 1999), BUDDE SONGS INCORPORATED, USA.
SCREEN GEMS-EMI MUSIC PUBLISHING LIMITED/BUCKS MUSIC GROUP LIMITED
ALL RIGHTS RESERVED. INTERNATIONAL COPYRIGHT SECURED.

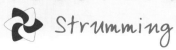

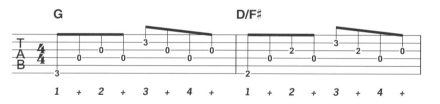

Justinguitar.com

Stage 1
Stage 2
Stage 3
Stage 4
Stage 5
Stage 6
Stage 7
Stage 8
Stage 9
Bonus

Introduction

This is Elvis Presley's comeback hit, recorded by The King in 1972.

Strumming

What a beautiful song this is, and it's lovely to play too. There are two acoustic guitar parts on the recording: a fingerpicking part and a strumming part (which I assume was played by Elvis). I recommend that you start by strumming, Elvis-style, simply playing all down-strums on even eighth-notes. It sounds like Elvis strummed using the fleshy part of his thumb, achieving a slightly rounder sound, which fits the mood of the song and creates further contrast with the fingerstyle guitar part.

Pay attention to the accents in the song—for example in the fourth bar of the verse, the C and D chords are played once each on beats 3 and 4 and the whole band joins it. Picking up these little things will add a professional touch! Watch out in the pre-chorus, where the chords change quite quickly. There are also a few starts and stops in the arrangement that are best learnt by ear.

Fingerstyle

In order to work out a suitable fingerstyle pattern, start with the bass note of the chord on beat 1 and then play other notes from the chord on the following eighth-note beats, and see what you come up with. You'll hear a lovely Dsus4 and a flick-off with the little finger when the rhythm part is strumming the D/F♯. Once you've found a pattern that works, you can try adding similar 'ornaments'.

Everybody Hurts

Words & Music by Peter Buck, Bill Berry, Mike Mills & Michael Stipe

♩.=63

Intro $^6_8$ ‖: D | D | G | G :‖

Verse 1
D   D   G   G
When your day is long,
        D   D   G   G
And the night, the night is yours a - lone.
D   D   G   G
   When you're sure you've had e - nough
        D   D   G │ G   G/F♯ │
Of this life,   well, hang on.

Chorus 1
Em   Em   A   A
Don't let yourself go,
Em   Em   A   A
'Cause everybody cries
Em   Em   A   A
And everybody hurts
            D   D G G   D   D   G
some - times,   sometimes everything is wrong,
G   (D)
   Now it's time to sing a - long.

Verse 2
When your day is night alone, if you feel like letting go.
If you think you've had too much, of this life, well, hang on.

Chorus 2
'Cause everybody hurts, take comfort in your friends.
And everybody hurts.

Bridge
F♯   F♯   Bm Bm F♯ F♯ Bm Bm
Don't throw your hand,   oh,   now,
F♯   F♯   Bm Bm
Don't throw your hand,
C   C   G   G
If you feel like you're a - lone,
C   │C   G/B │ Am   Am
No, no, no, you're not a - lone.

Verse 3
If you're on your own in this life, the days and nights are long.
When you think you've had too much, of this life to hang on.

Chorus 3
Well, everybody hurts, sometimes, everybody cries.
And everybody hurts
            D   D G   G   D   D   G   G
Some - times,   and everybody hurts   some - times.

Outro
(G)   D   D   G   G
So hold   on,   hold   on,
           D   D   G   G
Hold   on,   hold   on...   *(Repeat, vocals ad lib. to fade)*

© COPYRIGHT 1992 NIGHT GARDEN MUSIC/UNI-CHAPPELL MUSIC, USA.
WARNER/CHAPPELL MUSIC LIMITED.
ALL RIGHTS RESERVED. INTERNATIONAL COPYRIGHT SECURED.

Stage 1 · Stage 2 · Stage 3 · Stage 4 · Stage 5 · Stage 6 · Stage 7 · Stage 8 · Stage 9 · Bonus

justinguitar.com

Stage 1
Stage 2
Stage 3
Stage 4
Stage 5
Stage 6
Stage 7
Stage 8
Stage 9
Bonus

Introduction

R.E.M.'s enduring ballad is a fantastic song for introducing beginners to fingerstyle guitar playing—it's a pretty simple (but effective) pattern, and should be easy enough to sing along to.

Fingerstyle

Although guitarist Peter Buck recorded this song using a pick, I'd like you use your fingers, as it will be good practice. We'll start with a slightly simplified pattern, using just your thumb on the bass note and fingers 1, 2 and 3 on strings 1, 2 and 3, as shown below. Be aware that we're in 6/8 time, meaning that we have six notes per bar, with the accents landing on beats 1 and 4.

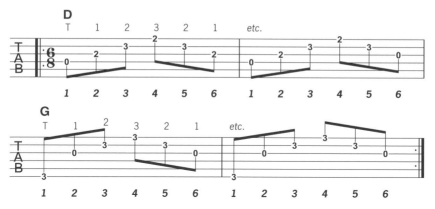

The G chord on the original recording uses a slightly different pattern:

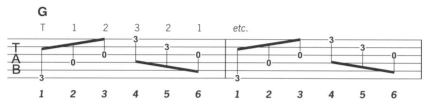

When moving to the chorus, we have a nice little run down to the Em chord.

continued...

Chorus

The chorus presents the same options as the verses—you can choose either the simpler or the original picking pattern, shown before.

(Simple version)

(Original version)

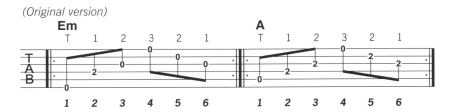

Don't forget the stops at the end of the chorus—these are vital moments in the song!

Bridge

The bridge presents a few problems in the form of some difficult barre chords but it shouldn't stop you enjoying this great song—just simplify the chords into power chords! The F# will become an F#5 and the Bm you will become a B5 power chord. On the original recording, you'll hear them on a slightly crunchy electric guitar, with the chords ringing out, but experiment and see what you prefer.

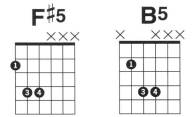

I Hope That I Don't Fall In Love With You
Words & Music by Tom Waits

Introduction

This is a wonderful melancholic ballad by Tom Waits, with some lovely
fingerstyle guitar parts.

Chords

There are a couple of interesting chords here to check out. They're
both versions of a G (dominant) chord, and have complicated names
but are not difficult to play. The F/G is an F chord with a G in the bass
and you just lift off one finger to move to the G9. You might find it a
little stretchy but it'll become much easier with a little practice.

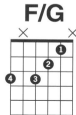
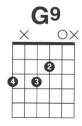
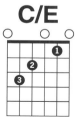
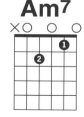

There are at least two guitars here and there's some lovely interplay
between them. We're going to start with the more consistent guitar part,
which more or less follows the same pattern, whereby the thumb plays
the lowest note of the chord (either on string 5 or string 6, depending
on the chord) and then finger 1 to 3 play the notes in between. The
pattern repeats itself every half bar. On the next page you'll see the
main chord sequence, written in TAB.

Stage 1
Stage 2
Stage 3
Stage 4
Stage 5
Stage 6
Stage 7
Stage 8
Stage 9
Bonus

I Hope That I Don't Fall In Love With You

Words & Music by Tom Waits

Stage 1 Stage 2 Stage 3 Stage 4 Stage 5 Stage 6 Stage 7 Stage 8 Stage 9 Bonus

♩=86

Intro

‖: C   F | F/G | G⁹   :‖

Verse 1

      |C   F |F/G   G⁹
Well I hope that I don't fall in love with you,
      |C   F |F/G   G⁹
'Cause falling in love just makes me blue.
      |F   C
Well the music plays and you display,
      |G   C
Your heart for me to see,
      |F   C/E   ²⁄₄|F   ⁴⁄₄|F/G   G⁹
I had a beer and now I hear you calling out for me.
      |C   F   G |C F/G | C G Am⁷ G/B |
And I hope that I don't fall in love with you.

Verse 2

Well the room is crowded, people everywhere,
And I wonder, should I offer you a chair?
Well if you sit down with this old clown,
Take that frown and break it,
Before the evening's gone away,
I think that we could make it.
And I hope that I don't fall in love with you.

Verse 3

Well the night does funny things inside a man,
These old tom-cat feelings you don't understand.
Well I turn around to look at you,
You light a cigarette.
I wish I had the guts to bum one,
But we've never met.
And I hope that I don't fall in love with you.

Verse 4

I can see that you are lonesome just like me,
And it being late, you'd like some company.
Well I turn around to look at you,
And you look back at me.
The guy you're with he's up and split,
The chair next to you's free.
And I hope that you don't fall in love with me.

Verse 5

(G/B)   C   C   ²⁄₄ F   ⁴⁄₄ F/G   G⁹
Now it's closing time,   the music's fading out,
      |C   F |F/G   G⁹
Last call for drinks, I'll have another stout.
      |F   C |
Well I turn around to look at you,

© COPYRIGHT 1973 FIFTH FLOOR MUSIC INCORPORATED, USA.
BMG RIGHTS MANAGEMENT (US) LLC.
ALL RIGHTS RESERVED. INTERNATIONAL COPYRIGHT SECURED.

cont.

```
|G                         C
    You're nowhere to be found.
|F                    C/E          | C/E
I search the place for your lost face,
            F           | F/G       | G9  Am7 G/B  |
Guess I'll have another round.        And  |
|C              F   2/4| G9      4/4|C    F/G      | C  G | C
Think that I just fell in love with you.
```

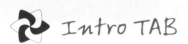 **Intro TAB**

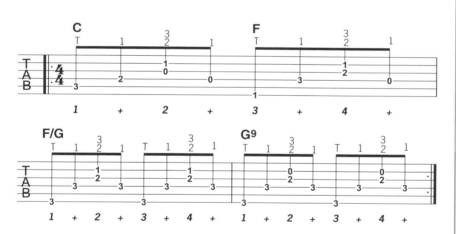

Of course you are free to experiment and play it your own way too—the TAB above is just a starting suggestion. You might also like to try strumming it (easy eighth-note strumming will work) but personally I much prefer this song fingerstyle.

There are other bits to keep you on your toes too: a 2/4 bar, which is half the length of a usual bar and might throw you off course if you aren't expecting it—you may also find the section at the end of the chorus, leading back into the verse, a bit challenging. Here the chords change on every beat, so will require some concentration.

Stage 1
Stage 2
Stage 3
Stage 4
Stage 5
Stage 6
Stage 7
Stage 8
Stage 9
Bonus

Give Me Love

Words & Music by Ed Sheeran, Christopher Leonard & Jake Gosling

Stage 1
Stage 2
Stage 3
Stage 4
Stage 5
Stage 6
Stage 7
Stage 8
Stage 9
Bonus

Capo Fret **1**

♩.=58

Verse 1

⁶⁄₈

Am   F   C   C
Give me love   like her,

Am   F   C   C
'Cause lately I've been waking up alone.

Am   F   C   C
Paint splattered teardrops on my shirt,

Am   F   C   C
Told you I'd let them go.

Pre-chorus 1

(C)   Dm   Dm
And that I'll fight my corner,

              F   F
Maybe to - night I'll call ya

           C   C   G   G
After my blood turns into alcohol,

    Dm   F
No, I just wanna hold ya.

Chorus 1

|C   Dm |F
  Give a little time to me or burn this out,

|C   Dm |F
  We'll play hide and seek to turn this around,

|C   Dm |F
  All I want is the taste that your lips allow.

|Am   G |F
  My, my,   my, my,   oh give me love.

Link 1

|Am   F |C
  My, my,   my, my,   oh give me love.

|Am   F |C
  My, my,   my, my,   oh give me love.

Verse 2

Give me love like never before,
'Cause lately I've been craving more.
And it's been a while but I still feel the same,
Maybe I should let you go.

Pre-chorus 2   As Pre-chorus 1

Chorus 2   As Chorus 1 *(Play x2)*

Link 2   As Link 1

Bridge

‖: Am |Am   G |
M-my my, m-my my, m-my my, give me love, lov - er.   :‖ *Play x16*

Outro

‖: Am   F
  My, my, my, my,   oh give me love.

C   C
  My, my, my, my,   oh give me love.   :‖

© COPYRIGHT 2011 BDI MUSIC LTD/SONY/ATV MUSIC PUBLISHING/WARNER/CHAPPELL MUSIC PUBLISHING LIMITED.
ALL RIGHTS RESERVED. INTERNATIONAL COPYRIGHT SECURED.

Introduction

Ed Sheeran wins again with another massive hit—man, can that guy write a great song. We're looking at the (slightly shorter) single edit of the track.

Strumming

This song is in 6/8 time, which may be new to you. Rather than four beats per bar, in 6/8 you have two groups of three beats, creating a kind of swaying, waltz-like feel. At the very start there are three 'pick up notes'—the pattern starts immediately afterwards, as the band comes in.

During the opening strumming pattern there are some individual notes picked out—I haven't marked them in as they're pretty tricky, but worth revisiting after you've looked at the 'Picked Fingerstyle' chapter in my *Intermediate Method* (IM-156).

Verse / Chorus pattern

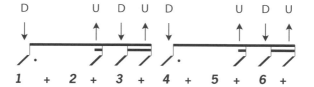

During the verse, this strumming pattern is actually part of a 4-bar cycle. The first three bars are identical, and use the pattern above. In the fourth bar, Ed adds some accents. You can also hit the note B (S5/F2) on the last note.

Bar 4 of Verse pattern

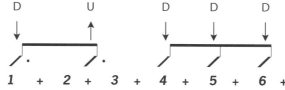

The pre-chorus has a few variations, then the chorus goes back to the first strumming pattern. At the end of the chorus, we have a slightly more gritty sound, where Ed plays all down-strums on the beat, just playing the lowest note (root note) of the chord.

On the second C chord in the verses you might like to add a little ornament. Lift finger 2 up on beat 1 and strum and then hammer the finger down. Finally, the bridge and outro have a very different feel, but you'll be fine to strum through them using the verse / chorus pattern.

Stage 1
Stage 2
Stage 3
Stage 4
Stage 5
Stage 6
Stage 7
Stage 8
Stage 9
Bonus

It's A Long Way To The Top (If You Wanna Rock 'N' Roll)

Words & Music by Angus Young, Malcolm Young & Bon Scott

Stage 1
Stage 2
Stage 3
Stage 4
Stage 5
Stage 6
Stage 7
Stage 8
Stage 9
Bonus

♩=138

Intro

riff ⸻

‖: A5 │ A5 │ A5 │ A5 :‖ *(Play x4)*

Verse 1

riff x8

Ridin' down the highway, goin' to a show,
Stop in all the by-ways, playin' rock 'n' roll.
Gettin' robbed, gettin' stoned,
Gettin' beat up, broken boned.
Gettin' had, gettin' took,
I tell you folks it's harder than it looks.

Chorus 1

    A5   │G5   D/F#   │A5 A5
It's a long way to the top if you wanna rock 'n' roll.
    A5   │G5   D/F#   │A5 A5
It's a long way to the top if you wanna rock 'n' roll.
    A5   A5   D/A
If you   think it's easy doin' one night stands,
            D/A
Try playin' in a rock roll band.
    G5   D/F#   A5 A5
It's a long way to the top if you wanna rock 'n' roll.

Solo
(bagpipes)

‖: A5 │ A5 │ A5 │ A5 :‖ *Play x6*

‖: G5 │ D/F# │ A5 │ A5 :‖ *Play x4*

│ A5 │ A5 │ A5 │ A5 │

Verse 3

Hotel, motel, make you wanna cry,
Ladies do the hard sell, know the reason why.
Gettin' old, gettin' grey,
Gettin' ripped off, under-paid.
Gettin' sold second hand,
That's how it goes, playin' in a band.

Chorus 3

It's a long way to the top if you wanna rock 'n' roll.
It's a long way to the top if you wanna rock 'n' roll.
    A5   A5   D/A
If you   wanna be a star of stage and screen,
            D/A
Look out it's rough and mean.
‖: G5   D/F#   A5 A5 :‖
It's a long way to the top if you wanna rock 'n' roll. *(Play x4)*

Outro

‖: A5 │ A5 │ A5 │ A5 :‖ *(Repeat to fade)*

(Vocals and bagpipes ad lib.)

G5

D/F#
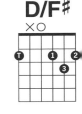

D/A

© COPYRIGHT 1976 J. ALBERT & SON PTY. LIMITED.
ALL RIGHTS RESERVED. INTERNATIONAL COPYRIGHT SECURED.

Stage 1

Stage 2

Stage 3

Stage 4

Stage 5

Stage 6

Stage 7

Stage 8

Stage 9

Bonus

Introduction

This AC/DC song is great fun to play and a good lesson on playing 'in the pocket'. The main riff isn't hard but it takes time and effort to make it 'sit' perfectly with the rest of the band. Be aware that the recording is slightly sped up, so that it sounds about a semitone sharp.

Riff and rhythm

The rhythm is the big deal here—it's the subtle muting and lifting of the chords that make it work so well and this is probably what you'll find yourself working on the most. Check out the TAB below and listen to the LEFT speaker (the greatest rock rhythm guitar player of all time, Malcolm Young) and really try to nail down that part. Play along, listen a lot and try and make it feel natural.

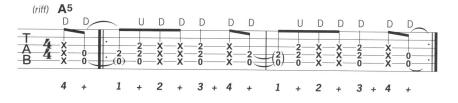

Chorus

The chorus uses big open chords, typical of AC/DC, all of which are played with down-strums. Make sure you hit the chords cleanly and let them ring out. Be careful to mute the appropriate strings, so only those shown are ringing out. On the D/F♯ I usually play the bass note with my thumb, which is what Malcolm Young seems to do.

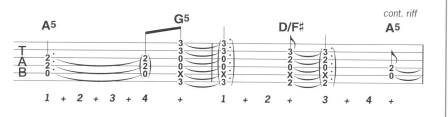

211

Romeo And Juliet

Words & Music by Mark Knopfler

Capo Fret

5

♩=86

Intro

```
   1 2 3 4   1 2 3 4   1 2 3 4   1 2 3 4
:‖ C    G  F    G  │ C    G  F    G :‖
```

Verse 1

```
 1    2         3    4    1       2         3       4
│C                     │ Am                       G       │
    A lovestruck Romeo       sings a streetsuss sere - nade,

 1    2         3    4  1    2         3       4
│C                   G │ Am                F                │
    Laying everybody low      with a lovesong that he made.

 1  2       3       4   1  2         3           4
│G                    F │ G               C                    │
    Finds a streetlight,   steps out of the shade, says something like

│F                      │ G                │
    'You and me babe, how a - bout it?'
```

Verse 2

Juliet says, 'Hey it's Romeo, you nearly gimme a heart attack.'
He's underneath the window, she's singing
'Hey la, my boyfriend's back,
You shouldn't come around here, singing up at people like that.'
'Anyway what you gonna to do about it?'

Chorus 1

```
     1 2 3     4         1       2       3    4
    │C    G          │ Am           F    G │
Juli - et,      the dice was loaded from the start, and I

 1 2 3       4         1       2       3       4    1  2 3  4
│C    G          │ Am          F       G │ C    F  │
Bet,      and you ex - ploded into my heart, and I for - get, I forget

 1  2           3   4
│Am              F        │
     The movie song.

 1  2               3       4    1         2      +    3    4
│Dm                       C    │ F                G    Am   G │
    When you gonna realise   it was just that the time was wrong,
```

Link

```
│C    G │ F    G │ C    G │ F    G │
   Juliet.
```

Verse 3

Come up on different streets, they both were streets of shame,
Both dirty, both mean, yes and the dream was just the same.
And I dreamed your dream for you and now your dream is real.
How can you look at me as if I was just another one of your deals?

Verse 4

When you can fall for chains of silver, you can fall for chains of gold,
You can fall for pretty strangers and the promises they hold.
You promised me everything, you promised me thick and thin,
Now you just say, 'Oh Romeo, yeah, you know,
I used to have a scene with him.'

Chorus 2

Juliet, when we made love you used to cry.
You said 'I love you like the stars above, I'll love you till I die.'
There's a place for us, you know the movie song,
When you gonna realise it was just that the time was wrong, Juliet?

© COPYRIGHT 1980 STRAITJACKET SONGS LIMITED.
UNIVERSAL MUSIC PUBLISHING LIMITED.
ALL RIGHTS RESERVED. INTERNATIONAL COPYRIGHT SECURED.

Stage 1 · Stage 2 · Stage 3 · Stage 4 · Stage 5 · Stage 6 · Stage 7 · Stage 8 · Stage 9 · Bonus

Stage 1
Stage 2
Stage 3
Stage 4
Stage 5
Stage 6
Stage 7
Stage 8
Stage 9
Bonus

Verse 6	And all I do is miss you and the way we used to be, All I do is keep the beat and bad company, All I do is kiss you Through the bars of a rhyme. Julie, I'd do the stars with you any time.
Chorus 3	Juliet, when we made love you used to cry. You said 'I love you like the stars above, I'll love you till I die.' There's a place for us, you know the movie song, When you gonna realise it was just that the time was wrong, Juliet?
Link	As Intro
Verse 7	As Verse 1
Outro	‖: F | G | F | G :‖ *Repeat ad lib. to fade*

Introduction

I'm a huge Mark Knopfler fan and this song is one of Dire Straits' finest. Unfortunately for a beginner the original version would be terrifying, as it's in open G tuning and uses complex fingerstyle techniques—I'd recommend saving the 'authentic' version until you've been playing for a few years! When you get there, I have a video which will take you through the song, step by step.

Strumming & counting

In the intro (and the link section) you'll often see two chords shown per bar but they're not evenly spaced—the second chord is played on beat 4, so you change chord a beat later than you might expect. This varies, so I've written the count on the music page for you—you should try to figure out the rhythm by listening to the song.

Intro / Verse strumming

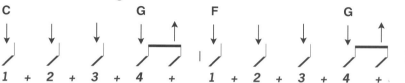

Chorus strumming

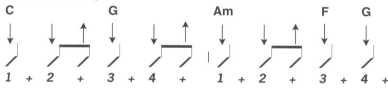

213

Skinny Love

Words & Music by Justin Vernon

♩=150

Intro

‖: Am | C | C/G | C/G :‖ *(Play x3)*

| D13(no 3) | D13(no 3) | Am | Am C |

| C/G | C/G | C | C |

Verse 1

Am   C   C/G   C/G
Come on skinny love just last the year,

Am   C   C/G   C/G
Pour a little salt we were never here.

        Am   C   C/G   C/G
My, my, my, my, my, my, my, my,

                  D13(no 3) D13(no 3)   Am   Am
Staring at the sink of blood and crushed veneer.

Link 1

| C | C | C | C |

Verse 2

I tell my love to wreck it all,
Cut out all the ropes and let me fall.
My, my, my, my, my, my, my, my,
Right in this moment this order's tall.

Chorus 1

          C   C   G6/B   Fmaj7/A
And I told you to be patient, and I told you to be fine.

          C   C   G6/B   Fmaj7/A
And I told you to be balanced, and I told you to be kind.

            C   C   G6/B   Fmaj7/A
And in the morning I'll be with you, but it will be a different kind.

           C   C
And I'll be holding all the tickets,

           G6/B   Fmaj7/A Fmaj7/A Fmaj7/A Fmaj7/A
And you'll be owing all the fines.

Verse 3

Come on skinny love what happened here?
Suckle on the hope in light brassieres,
My, my, my, my, my, my, my, my,
Sullen load is full; so slow on the split.

Link 1

| C | C | C | C |

Chorus 2

And I told you to be patient, and I told you to be fine.
And I told you to be balanced, and I told you to be kind.
And now all your love is wasted, and then who the hell was I?
And I'm breaking at the britches, and at the end of all your lines.

Chorus 3

Who will love you? Who will fight? Who will fall far behind?

Outro

‖: Am | C | C/G | C/G :‖ *(Play x3)*

| D13(no 3) | D13(no 3) | Am | Am C | C |

© COPYRIGHT 2008 APRIL BASE PUBLISHING, USA.
KOBALT MUSIC PUBLISHING LIMITED.
ALL RIGHTS RESERVED. INTERNATIONAL COPYRIGHT SECURED.

Stage 1
Stage 2
Stage 3
Stage 4
Stage 5
Stage 6
Stage 7
Stage 8
Stage 9
Bonus

justinguitar.com

Stage 1
Stage 2
Stage 3
Stage 4
Stage 5
Stage 6
Stage 7
Stage 8
Stage 9
Bonus

Introduction

This song by Bon Iver uses an open tuning, but it's fun to play and works great in normal tuning using (almost) standard chords. The original is in open G tuning and is slightly flat (you'll find more on open tunings on my website) so you'll find that what you play on your guitar won't exactly match the recording.

Chords

There are a few new chords—play the C/G just like a normal C, but move your finger 3 onto string 6 and mute string 5. It's the best way to replicate the open tuning sound for that grip. The D13(no3) is a complex name for a pretty simple chord, just a D with fingers 2 and 3 taken off. It's not exactly what (frontman) Justin Vernon plays but it's pretty close.

In the chorus we have a G6/B, which is like a regular G/B, which you might have seen before, but with the open E ringing out. The Fmaj7/A is a fairly common grip with nothing tricky except for its name!

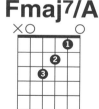

Strumming

Your strumming should be very loose and relaxed and based roughly on the pattern below. Allow yourself to add more strums and let the music ebb and flow, getting louder and softer. Try to let the music breathe—this is especially important for this sparse style.

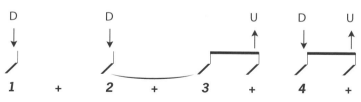

Stand By Me

Words & Music by Noel Gallagher

Stage 1
Stage 2
Stage 3
Stage 4
Stage 5
Stage 6
Stage 7
Stage 8
Stage 9
Bonus

♩=85

Intro ‖: G │ B7 │ C C/B │ D :‖

Verse 1
G   B7
Made a meal and threw it up on Sunday,
│C   C/B   │D
I've gotta lot of things to learn.
G   B7
  Said I would and I'll be leaving one day,
│C   C/B   │D
Before my heart starts to   burn.

Pre-chorus 1
C   D
  So what's the matter with you?
│G   D/F♯   │Em
Sing me something new.
A
Don't you know the cold and wind and rain don't know,
C   D   D
They only seem to come and go a - way.

Verse 2
Times are hard when things have got no meaning,
I've found a key upon the floor.
Maybe you and I will not believe in
The things we find behind the door.

Pre-chorus 2 As Pre-chorus 1

Chorus 1
G   D   Am
  Stand by me, nobody knows,
          ¾│C   F   D/F♯ │
The way it's gonna be.
G   D   Am
  Stand by me, nobody knows,
          ¾│C   F   D/F♯ │
The way it's gonna be.
⁴⁄₄ G   D   Am
  Stand by me, nobody knows,
          ¾│C   F   D/F♯ │
The way it's gonna be.
⁴⁄₄ G   D   Am
  Stand by me, nobody knows,
Am   C   D   (G)
  Yeah, nobody knows,   the way it's gonna be.

Link │G   │G   │

Verse 3
If you're leaving, will you take me with you?
I'm tired of talking on my phone.
There is one thing I can never give you,
My heart will never be your home.

C/B

Cadd9

© COPYRIGHT 1997 CREATION SONGS LIMITED/OASIS MUSIC (GB).
SONY/ATV MUSIC PUBLISHING.
ALL RIGHTS RESERVED. INTERNATIONAL COPYRIGHT SECURED.

Pre-chorus 3	As Pre-chorus 2
Chorus 2	As Chorus 1

Middle

|Em D|Cadd9 |Em   D|Cadd9
(be)   The way it's gonna be, yeah,
                         |Em   D|Cadd9
Maybe I can see, yeah.
                                  A
Don't you know the cold and wind and rain don't know,
        C   D   D
They only seem to come and go a - way.   Hey, hey!

Chorus 4	As Chorus 1

 # Introduction

This Oasis classic has some cool twists in it that should keep you occupied!

 # Intro / Verse strumming

The chords are fairly straightforward, meaning that the fun starts when we get into the rhythm. Nevertheless, get used to the chord sequence by strumming through the song, using four down-strums per bar, as normal.

This will soon reveal that the chorus has a few 3/4 bars, which have just 3 beats in them—for these you'll just be playing three down-strums, one on each chord. Then try this pattern below, which is a slightly simplified version of the intro and verse pattern on the recording.

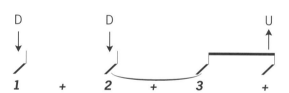

D		D		U	D	
1	+	2	+	3	+	4	+

continued...

Stage 1
Stage 2
Stage 3
Stage 4
Stage 5
Stage 6
Stage 7
Stage 8
Stage 9
Bonus

217

Stage 1 Stage 2 Stage 3 Stage 4 Stage 5 Stage 6 Stage 7 Stage 8 Stage 9 Bonus

Verse strumming (cont'd)

The previous pattern is part of a 4-bar sequence. Towards the end of the sequence, the D chord is pushed forward an eighth-note, as shown below. The push is repeated in the pre-chorus on the Em chord.

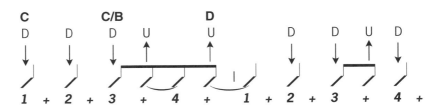

Chorus Strumming

The chorus strumming pattern is as follows, except in the 3/4 bars where you'll just use three down- strums, one on each chord.

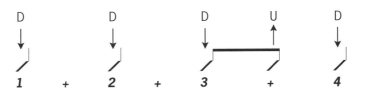

Sixteenth-note strumming

The 'actual' intro/verse strumming pattern is a sixteenth-note pattern, included for more advanced players. For this pattern you should move your hand twice as fast, keeping it moving all the time but hitting the strings as shown below. This will mean that you use all down-strums in the chorus.

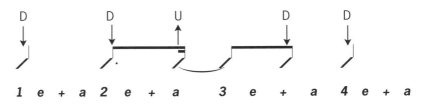

Take Me To Church

Words & Music by Andrew Hozier-Byrne

 ## Introduction

Hozier's poignant single is a seriously powerful song. I heard it first on the radio but it was the music video that got my attention and made me listen again to the lyrics. It's also a fun song to play with its fair share of surprises.

 ## Strumming & counting

We start off in 6/4 time, which means simply counting an extra two beats more than you would in good old 4/4 time. Notice that the second chord happens on beat 5, so the first chord is held for four beats and then the second for just two beats. Knowing this is key to understanding the rhythm pattern.

 ## 'Tag' and power chords

Watch out for the 'tag' at the end of the verse, where it goes back to 4/4. It flows pretty naturally but may still throw you off if you don't understand what is going on. Rhythmically, I'd recommend strumming on the change of chord and letting it ring out (like it does on the record), but feel free to experiment too.

Linking into the chorus are some power chords with an interesting rhythm—I've written it below with the count. This section isn't difficult but it is slightly unexpected, and may require some focused practice.

Stage 1
Stage 2
Stage 3
Stage 4
Stage 5
Stage 6
Stage 7
Stage 8
Stage 9
Bonus

Stage 1
Stage 2
Stage 3
Stage 4
Stage 5
Stage 6
Stage 7
Stage 8
Stage 9
Bonus

Take Me To Church
Words & Music by Andrew Hozier-Byrne

♩=125

Verse 1

$^6_4$ |Em   Am |Em   Am |
My lover's got humour,   she's the giggle at a funeral.

|G   Am |
Knows everybody's disap - proval,

|Em   Am |
I should've worshipped her sooner.

|Em   Am |Em   Am |
If the heavens ever did speak,   she's the last true mouthpiece.

|G   Am |Em   Am |
Every Sunday's getting more bleak,   a fresh poison each week.

$^4_4$ D   C
We were born sick,   you heard them say it,

Verse 2

$^6_4$ |Em   Am |Em |
My church offers no abso - lutes.

Am |
She tells me, worship in the bedroom.

|G   Am |Em   Am |
The only heaven I'll be sent to   is when I'm alone with you.

$^4_4$ D   C   (C)   (C) |
I was born sick,   but I love it,   command me to be well.

Pre-chorus

$^6_4$ | G   C |G   C |G   Cm $^4_4$|G |
A -   A - men. A - men. A - men.

Chorus 1

|G5   F♯5   F5 |Em   Em   B7
Take me to church, I'll worship like a dog at the shrine of your lies

     B7   G
I'll tell you my sins and you can sharpen your knife.

     Am
Offer me my deathless death,

     Em |A5   G5
Good God, let me give you my life.

     F♯5 |Em   Em   B7
Take me to church, I'll worship like a dog at the shrine of your lies,

     B7   G
I'll tell you my sins so you can sharpen your knife.

     Am
Offer me my deathless death,

     Em |A5   G5   F♯5 |
Good God, let me give you my life.

Verse 3
(chords as Verse 2)

If I'm a pagan of the good times, my lover's the sunlight.
To keep the goddess on my side, she demands a sacrifice.
Drain the whole sea, get something shiny.

Cm

© COPYRIGHT 2013 THE EVOLVING MUSIC COMPANY LIMITED.
SONY/ATV MUSIC PUBLISHING.
ALL RIGHTS RESERVED. INTERNATIONAL COPYRIGHT SECURED.

Verse 4
(chords as Verse 2)

Something meaty for the main course,
That's a fine looking high horse.
What you got in the stable? We've a lot of starving faithful.
That looks tasty, that looks plenty, this is hungry work.

Chorus 2

As Chorus 1

Bridge

| C | G | | B7 | Em |
No masters   or kings when the ritual be - gins,

      C   G   B7   Em
There is no sweeter innocence than our gentle sin.

     C   G   B7   Em
In the madness and soil of that   sad earthly scene,

    C   G   B7   Em   Em
Only then I am human, only then I am clean.

    C   C $\frac{6}{4}$|G C |G Cm |G   Cm |G
Oh,   oh,   A - men. A - men. A - men.

Chorus 3

As Chorus 1 *(Final chord Em)*

Chorus / bridge

During the chorus, I would use all down-strums on even eighth-notes to create some momentum and to act as a contrast against the sparse verses.

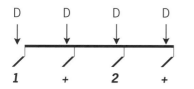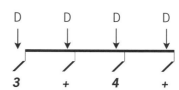

The only other section is the bridge, where you will probably want to continue the eighth-note down- strums, and build up the dynamics even more.

There are some fantastic solo acoustic performances of this song on YouTube, so check out the way that Hozier plays it and see which aspects of it you'd like to bring into your own playing. Notice that he uses a mixture of open chords and barre chords, which you might like to try too if you are familiar with the different grips.

Stage 1
Stage 2
Stage 3
Stage 4
Stage 5
Stage 6
Stage 7
Stage 8
Stage 9
Bonus

Stage 1
Stage 2
Stage 3
Stage 4
Stage 5
Stage 6
Stage 7
Stage 8
Stage 9
Bonus

 ## Introduction

In this Bonus Stage we are just taking a little extra time to consolidate what you (hopefully!) already know. Well done on making it this far—I really hope you are feeling confident with it all. If not, now is the time to go and revise and single out anything that you are struggling with. My advice is to pick songs that you found hard and work on them until you get them right. You will find that perfecting one song will help you play many of the other songs, because the skills you've learnt in one song are likely to be required in other songs.

There are some super-cool tunes in this bonus stage. Some are a bit tricky, and diverge a little from how we've learnt songs so far, but you're are up for a challenge, aren't you?

A couple of the songs ('Wicked Game' and 'Proud Mary') utilise a barre B minor chord. I've purposely left barre chords out of the *Beginner's Course*, but thought I'd give you a little preview of what comes next! Barre chords are covered in detail in Stage 1 of my *Intermediate Method*.

 ## Bonus Songs: Your notes

World Where You Live

Words & Music by Neil Finn

Introduction

This classic Crowded House tune is wonderful song and a lot of fun to play. The verses on the original recording feature a lot of keyboard, but the part works really well on acoustic guitar as well.

Strumming

As with most Crowded House songs there are a few quirks to watch out for, including a couple of sneaky 2/4 bars and some rhythm feels that you'll have to adapt to. For the intro and verse you can keep things very simple, strumming just one chord per bar, and letting it ring out. 'Old Faithful' (page 19) will also work as a starting point, which you could then develop.

The 2/4 bar preceding the chorus is made more awkward by the 'push' on the first Am of the chorus. The 'push' means that the chord is played earlier than expected: on the '+' after 4 in the previous bar. It's essential that you listen to the recording, though I've also written out a suggested strumming pattern for that section.

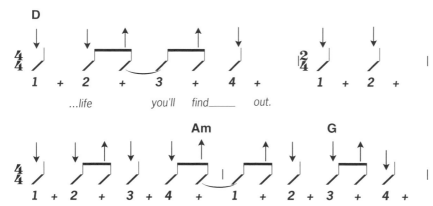

For the chorus you'll probably want to develop the strumming further. I would recommend keeping to this simple pattern as it will be easier to join on to the pattern above.

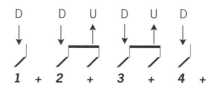

Stage 1
Stage 2
Stage 3
Stage 4
Stage 5
Stage 6
Stage 7
Stage 8
Stage 9
Bonus

World Where You Live

Words & Music by Neil Finn

♩=110

Stage 1
Stage 2
Stage 3
Stage 4
Stage 5
Stage 6
Stage 7
Stage 8
Stage 9
Bonus

Intro

| Em | Em | Em | Em |

Verse 1

```
Em                Em
Here's someone now who's got the muscle,
D           D
   His steady hand could move a mountain.
Em            Em
   Expert in bed, but come on now,
         D                       D
There must be something missing.
Em            Em              D          2/4 D
   That golden one leads a double   life, you'll find out.
```

Chorus 1

```
4/4 D                               |Am    G | D
    Tell me, I don't know where you go,
                     |G      A | D
Do you climb into space
                     |Am    G | D
To the world where you live?
                   |G    A |(Em)
The world where you live, oh - ooh.
```

Link

| Em | Em | Em | Em |

Verse 2

```
So here we lie against each other
And these four walls can never hold us.
We're looking for wide open spaces
High above the kitchen.
And we're strangers here
On our way to some other place.
```

Chorus 2

```
But I don't know where you go,
Do you climb into space
To the world where you live?
                   |G    A | D
The world where you live, oh - oh
                 |Em   D/F#   G  |
To the world where you live.
```

Bridge

```
A              D
Friends come 'round,
     Em         Fmaj7
You might re - member and be sad.
     A          D      Em    Fmaj7  Fmaj7  Fmaj7
Be - hind their eyes is unfa - miliar.
```

Instr.

|: Am G | D | Am G | D   :|

© COPYRIGHT 1986 ROUNDHEAD MUSIC, USA.
KOBALT MUSIC PUBLISHING LIMITED.
ALL RIGHTS RESERVED. INTERNATIONAL COPYRIGHT SECURED.

Stage 1
Stage 2
Stage 3
Stage 4
Stage 5
Stage 6
Stage 7
Stage 8
Stage 9
Bonus

Chorus 3

           | G   A | D
Do you climb into space

           | Am   G | D
To the world where you live?

          | G   A | D
The world where you live, oh-oh.

           | G   A | D
To the world where you live, yeah, yeah.

           | G   A | D
To the world where you live, hey, hey.

           G   D
To the world where you live.

           B♭5   C
To the world where you live.

           G | G   D |
To the world where you live.

Bridge

As we get to the bridge, we have a really cool rhythm that isn't too tricky but might throw you slightly off course if you're not expecting it.

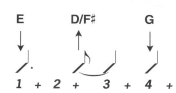

On the bridge I'd recommend playing down-strums on every numbered beat (four per bar). For the D and Em chords, you can use conventional chord grips, or if you want a challenge, use the original voicings below (the D becomes a Dadd9, and the Em becomes an Em/A).

The B♭5 is a sneak preview of a 'power chord', which we'll look at properly in Stage 7, and isn't tricky at all.

Stage 1
Stage 2
Stage 3
Stage 4
Stage 5
Stage 6
Stage 7
Stage 8
Stage 9
Bonus

Best Of You

Words & Music by Dave Grohl, Taylor Hawkins, Nate Mendel & Chris Shiflett

♩=130

Verse 1

N.C.   C#m7   C#m7
I've got another con - fession to make,

A5add9   A5add9
I'm your fool,

C#m7   C#m7
Everyone's got their chains to break,

A5add9   A5add9
Holding you.

B5add4   B5add4   A5add9   A5add9
Were you born to re - sist,   or be a - bused?

Chorus 1

(A5add9)   C#m7   B5add4   A5add9
   Is someone getting the best, the best, the best, the best of you?

A5add9   C#m7
   Is someone getting the best, the best,

B5add4   A5add9   A5add9
The best, the best of you?

C#m7   B5add4   A5add9   A5add9
Are you gone and on to someone new?

Verse 2

I needed somewhere to hang my head, without your noose.
You gave me something that I didn't have, but had no use.
I was too weak to give in, too strong to lose.

Verse 3

My heart is under arrest again, but I break loose.
My head is giving me life or death, but I can't choose.
I swear I'll never give in, I refuse.

Chorus 2

(A5add9)   C#m7   B5add4   A5add9
   Is someone getting the best, the best, the best, the best of you?

F#7add11   C#m7   B5add4   A5add9
   Is someone getting the best, the best, the best, the best of you?

F#7add11   C#m7
   Has someone taken your faith, it's real,

B5add4   A5add9   F#7add11
The pain you feel, your trust, you must con - fess.

C#m7
Is someone getting the best, the best,

B5add4   A5add9   F#7add11
the best, the best of you?   Oh...

Interlude

| C#m7 | C#m7 | A5add9 | A5add9 |

| C#m7 | C#m7 | A5add9 | F#7add11 |

‖: B5add4 | B5add4 | A5add9 | A5add9 :‖
Oh...   Oh...

© COPYRIGHT 2005 FLYING EARFORM MUSIC/MJ TWELVE MUSIC/SONGS OF UNIVERSAL INCORPORATED/LIVING
UNDER A ROCK MUSIC/I LOVE THE PUNK ROCK MUSIC.
BUG MUSIC LIMITED/UNIVERSAL/MCA MUSIC LIMITED.
ALL RIGHTS RESERVED. INTERNATIONAL COPYRIGHT SECURED.

Chorus 3	Has someone taken your faith, it's real, the pain you feel?
(chords as Chorus 2)	The life, the love, you die to heal.
	The hope that stops, the broken hearts,
	Your trust, you must confess.
	Is someone getting the best, the best, the best, the best of you?
	Is someone getting the best, the best, the best, the best of you?

Verse 4	I've got another confession my friend,
	I'm no fool.
	I'm getting tired of starting again,
	Somewhere new.
	Were you born to resist, or be abused?

B5add4   B5add4   A5add9 | A5add9 N.C. |

I swear I'll never give in,   I re - fuse.

Chorus 3	As Chorus 2
Outro	‖: C♯m7	C♯m7	C♯m7	C♯m7 :‖

Stage 1 · Stage 2 · Stage 3 · Stage 4 · Stage 5 · Stage 6 · Stage 7 · Stage 8 · Stage 9 · Bonus

 ## Introduction

This is a rock masterpiece from the incredibly talented Dave Grohl, and his band Foo Fighters. The song has some really interesting things going on, and fortunately it's not too tricky for a progressing beginner.

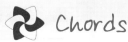 ## Chords

The big deal here is that the thinnest two strings are left open, and will ring out for most of the chords. Let's start by looking at the chord grips. The C♯m7 is a complicated name and may seem unfamiliar, but it's not hard to play—just make sure your finger 3 is not muting string 4. To get to the A5add9 leave finger 4 down and move finger 1 into position. To reach the B5add4, leave finger 4 down again and add fingers 1 and 3.

The only slightly tricky one comes later in the song, the F♯7add11. Look at the chord box (on the next page)—it's pretty much a B power chord shape but you should add one finger, making it similar to an easy barre chord shape. The changes are pretty easy actually—as usual they might take some practice but everything worth playing does!

Best Of You (cont'd)

Stage 1

Stage 2

Stage 3

Stage 4

Stage 5

Stage 6

Stage 7

Stage 8

Stage 9

Bonus

Chords (cont'd)

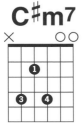
C#m7

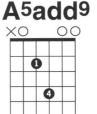
A5add9

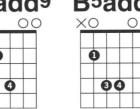
B5add4

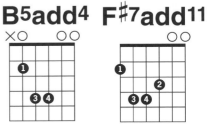
F#7add11

Rhythm

The rhythm is also superb (as you would expect from one of the world's greatest rock drummers!). You'll be using all down-strums and focusing on the thickest string of each chord grip, which you'll accent, but also push through the chords a little more so that you include all of the strings. It's a great technique to learn and sounds really cool, especially when combined with the open strings, which will continue to ring out through the pattern.

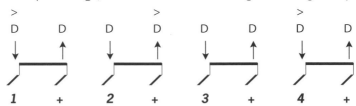

As with most Foo Fighters songs there are more interesting rhythms happening at various points but it's going to be easiest to learn these by listening to them—writing them out would probably make them seem more complicated than they are.

If you are getting into transcribing there are some excellent overdubbed parts using octaves, which are fun to transcribe and closely related to the power chord shapes.

Black Night
Words & Music by Ritchie Blackmore, Ian Gillan,
Roger Glover, Jon Lord & Ian Paice

Introduction

This Deep Purple classic is seriously fun to play on the guitar. It's much
more riff-based than what we've done so far in the book but it's a great taster
of this kind of riff-rock playing.

Riff 1

So let's start by looking at Riff 1. It uses only fingers 1 and 3; there's
nothing tricky here except for one 'fold', where you flatten ('fold') finger 3
from playing a note on string 5 with the tip of your finger to play a note on
string 4 for which you'll use the pad rather than the tip of your finger. It
might feel a bit strange if you've not done that kind of movement before.
It's important to play the rhythm correctly so I have written the count
under the riff for you. Play it slowly and get it right before speeding up.

(Em)

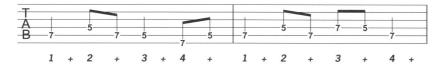

Riff 2 is the main riff under the verses and consists of a power chord,
moving between the D5 and E5, playing mostly the off beats. Make sure
you mute the strings on the beat to keep that rhythm going.

D5 E5   **D5 E5**

Stage 1

Stage 2

Stage 3

Stage 4

Stage 5

Stage 6

Stage 7

Stage 8

Stage 9

Bonus

Black Night

Words & Music by Ritchie Blackmore, Ian Gillan,
Roger Glover, Jon Lord & Ian Paice

Stage 1

Stage 2

Stage 3

Stage 4

Stage 5

Stage 6

Stage 7

Stage 8

Stage 9

♩=136

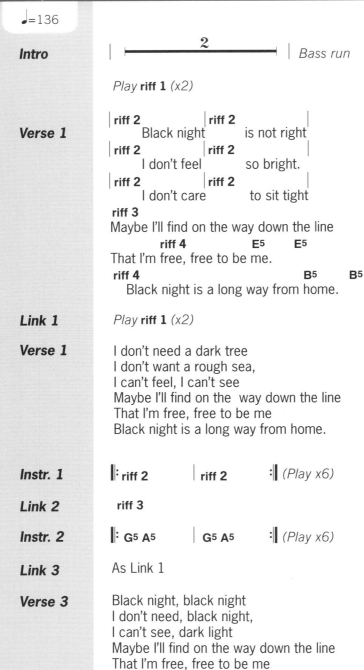

Intro | —————— **2** —————— | *Bass run*

Play **riff 1** *(x2)*

Verse 1

| **riff 2** | **riff 2** |
    Black night   is not right

| **riff 2** | **riff 2** |
    I don't feel   so bright.

| **riff 2** | **riff 2** |
    I don't care   to sit tight

riff 3
Maybe I'll find on the way down the line

       riff 4   **E5**   **E5**
That I'm free, free to be me.

    riff 4   **B5**   **B5**
   Black night is a long way from home.

Link 1   *Play* **riff 1** *(x2)*

Verse 1

I don't need a dark tree
I don't want a rough sea,
I can't feel, I can't see
Maybe I'll find on the way down the line
That I'm free, free to be me
Black night is a long way from home.

Instr. 1   ‖: **riff 2** | **riff 2** :‖ *(Play x6)*

Link 2   **riff 3**

Instr. 2   ‖: **G5 A5** | **G5 A5** :‖ *(Play x6)*

Link 3   As Link 1

Verse 3

Black night, black night
I don't need, black night,
I can't see, dark light
Maybe I'll find on the way down the line
That I'm free, free to be me
Black night is a long way from home.

Outro   ‖: **riff 2** :‖ *(Repeat to fade)*

© COPYRIGHT 1970 (RENEWED 1998) B. FELDMAN & CO. LTD. TRADING AS HEC MUSIC.
ALL RIGHTS FOR THE UNITED STATES AND CANADA CONTROLLED AND ADMINISTERED BY GLENWOOD MUSIC CORP.
ALL RIGHTS RESERVED. INTERNATIONAL COPYRIGHT SECURED.

Riff 3

Riff 3 works as a link, taking us to the 'refrain' of the song. This riff is probably the hardest in the song, but don't be scared of it, and don't be surprised if it takes you a little longer to master than the main riff. The last three notes are what are called a 'crotchet triplet': three notes played over two beats. The easiest way to learn it is to listen and copy the original recording but you can count it as shown below.

(E5)

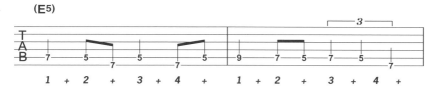

Riff 4

Riff 4 is the 'refrain' of the song and starts using an A octave shape, then the riff moves to G and then chugs on an open E power chord. The original guitar part has some lead fills on the E chord but they're well beyond the remit of a beginner songbook. On the final B chord there is a bit of action with the whammy bar which you can imitate if you have one. Just press it down a little bit, following the recording.

(A5)   **(G5)**

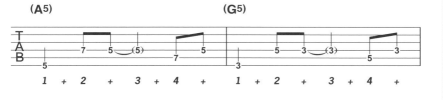

Bohemian Like You

Words & Music by Courtney Taylor-Taylor

♩=131

Intro

‖: (B) | (D) | (A) | (E) :‖

Play **riff** x2

| B | B | B | B | |

(You've got a great...)

Verse 1

                        B   D

You've got a great car, yeah, what's wrong with it today?

   A   E

I used to have one too, maybe I'll come and have a look.

      B   D

I really love your hairdo, yeah,

   A   E

I'm glad you like mine too, see, we're looking pretty cool. Getcha.

Link 1

| B | B | B | B | |

(So what do you...)

Verse 2

So what do you do? Oh yeah, I wait tables too.
No, I haven't heard your band 'cause you guys are pretty new.
But if you dig on vegan food, well, come over to my work,
I'll have them cook you something that you really love.

Chorus 1

B   D   A

(Love) 'cause I like you, yeah I like you,

      E   B

And I'm feeling so bohemian like you.

      D   A   E

Yeah I like you, yeah I like you, and I feel wa-ho, whoo!

Link 2

Play **riff** x2

| B | B | B | B | |

(Wait!)

Verse 3

Wait! Who's that guy just hanging at your pad?
He's looking kind of bummed. Yeah, you broke up? That's too bad.
I guess it's fair if he always pays the rent
And he doesn't get bent about sleeping on the couch when I'm (there).

Chorus 2

As Chorus 1

Link 3

Play **riff** x2

Chorus 3

And I'm getting wise and I feel so bohemian like you.
It's you that I want so please,
Just a casual, casual easy thing. Is it? It is for me.
And I like you, yeah I like you, and I like you, I like you,
I like you, I like you, I like you, I like you, I like you
And I feel who-hoa, whoo!

Outro

Play **riff** x2

| B | B | B | B | B | ‖

© COPYRIGHT 2000 CHRYSALIS MUSIC LIMITED.
ALL RIGHTS RESERVED. INTERNATIONAL COPYRIGHT SECURED.

Stage 1
Stage 2
Stage 3
Stage 4
Stage 5
Stage 6
Stage 7
Stage 8
Stage 9
Bonus

justinguitar.com

Stage 1
Stage 2
Stage 3
Stage 4
Stage 5
Stage 6
Stage 7
Stage 8
Stage 9
Bonus

Introduction

This Dandy Warhols song has a great riff, heavily influenced by the Rolling Stones, and as such works really well when played using Ketih Richards' favourite open G tuning. To tune to open G there's a lesson on my website (ES-031) or see page 119 for a brief rundown.

Chords and riff

All the chords are played just barring across all the strings from 5 to 1, and you need to mute string 6 with the tip of finger 1.

B is played at fret 4, **D** at fret 7, **A** at fret 2 and **E** at fret 9.

The riff is based on sus4 chords. You can get even more of a Keith Richards feel by adding two fingers in front of the barre chord, then lifting them off. Putting them down creates a '6sus4' chord but the name is arbitrary, it's just a chord, and not a hard one at that!

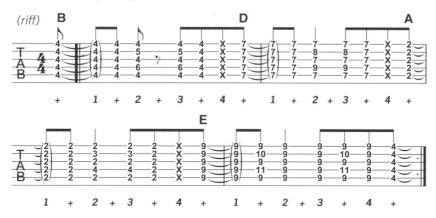

Single line riff

There's also one other little riff which is a single line, overdubbed, which can be played in open tuning too. Here's the TAB, still in open G tuning:

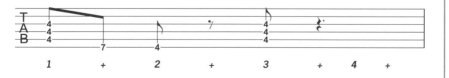

Stage 1
Stage 2
Stage 3
Stage 4
Stage 5
Stage 6
Stage 7
Stage 8
Stage 9
Bonus

Drops Of Jupiter (Tell Me)

Words & Music by Jimmy Stafford, Scott Underwood,
Patrick Monahan, Robert Hotchkiss & Clifford Colin

♩=80

Intro | C | G | F | F |

Verse 1
    C
Now that she's back in the atmosphere
    G   F   F
With drops of Jupiter in her hair, hey.
    C
She acts like summer and walks like rain,
    G   F   F
Re - minds me that there's a time to change, hey.
C
Since the return from her stay on the moon,
    G   F   F
She listens like spring and she talks like June, hey,   hey.

Chorus 1
  |G   A |D
But tell me, did you sail across the sun?
                      C |F
Did you make it to the Mil - ky Way, to see the lights all faded
C
   And that heaven is overrated?
|G   A |D   Dm7
Tell me, did you fall for a shoot - ing star? One without a permanent scar
                               F   (C)
And then you missed me, while you were looking for yourself out there.

Link 1 | C | G | F | F |

Verse 2
Now that she's back from that soul vacation,
Tracing her way through the constellation, hey.
She checks out Mozart while she does Tae-Bo,
Reminds me that there's room to grow, hey,
Now that she's back in the atmosphere,
I'm afraid that she might think of me as
F7
Plain ol' Jane told a story about a man
       F7
Who was too afraid to fly so he never did land.

F7

Chorus 2
But tell me, did the wind sweep you off your feet?
Did you finally get the chance to dance along the light of day
And head back to the Milky Way?
And tell me, did Venus blow your mind?
Was it everything you wanted to find?
And then you missed me while you were looking for yourself out there.

Link 2 | C | G | F | F |

Bridge
(F)   C
Can you imagine no love, pride, deep-fried chicken,
    G   F
Your best friend always sticking up for you

234

© COPYRIGHT 2001 BLUE LAMP MUSIC/EMI BLACKWOOD MUSIC INC/EMI APRIL MUSIC INC.
EMI MUSIC PUBLISHING LIMITED.
ALL RIGHTS RESERVED. INTERNATIONAL COPYRIGHT SECURED.

justinguitar.com

Stage 1

Stage 2

Stage 3

Stage 4

Stage 5

Stage 6

Stage 7

Stage 8

Stage 9

Bonus

F
Even when I know you're wrong?

     C
Can you imagine no first dance, freeze-dried romance,

G
Five-hour phone conversation,

  B♭5   **F**
The best soy latte that you ever had, and me?

Chorus 3   But tell me, did the wind sweep you off your feet?
        Did you finally get the chance to dance along the light of day
        And head back toward the Milky Way?

Chorus 4   As Chorus 1

        C   **G**   **F**
Outro   (Na-na, na-na, na-na, na-na, na-na, na-na, na-na-na.)

                   F
        And did you finally get the chance to dance along the light of day?
        C   **G**
        (Na-na, na-na, na-na, na-na, na-na, na-na)
         F   **F**
        And did you fall for a shooting star? Fall for a shooting star?
        C   **G**
        (Na-na, na-na, na-na, na-na, na-na, na-na)
           B♭5   **F**
        And now you're lonely looking for yourself out there.

 ## Introduction

This was Train's breakthrough single, released in 2002.

 ## Playing the off beats

There are some interesting changes of harmony and rhythm in this song—it can be played quite simply or made more complex for more advanced guitarists.

As usual, your first step is to play through the song using four simple down-strums to the bar, in order to get those chords and changes under your fingers. As you play along you're going to encounter some bits that feel strange or awkward, and we'll deal with them shortly!

continued...

Eighth-note strumming

Once you have mastered the basic strumming, I recommend that you start playing eighth-notes with all down-strums, as shown below. Once you are confident with that you might like to add in a few soft up-strums too, but the focus here is keeping your hand moving consistently.

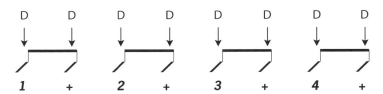

Sixteenth-note strumming

Once you're confident with keeping your hand moving, try this pattern (below). You'll hear it quite regularly on the original recording, although there are many subtle variations to it.

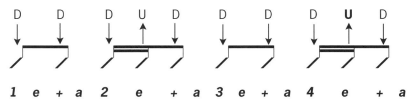

Your first real challenge is the accented chords in the chorus: the A moving to D and the C moving to F. The whole band pick up on these accents, and they're essential to the song. These accents occur immediately after beat 4, on the beat marked 'e', which I've highlighted above, and they are played with an up-strum. You'll let the chord ring, and in doing so miss out the usual following down-strum. So just to clarify—you'll use the above pattern but leave off that last down-strum. Your hand will keep moving as usual but won't be hitting the strings.

Hold Back The River
Words & Music by James Bay & Iain Archer

Stage 1

Stage 2

Stage 3

Stage 4

Stage 5

Stage 6

Stage 7

Stage 8

Stage 9

Bonus

 Introduction

James Bay's signature song involves getting up the 'dusty' end of the guitar, with some more advanced chord grips. You'll need to detune your guitar by a tone in order to play along with the recording (strings low to high: DGCFAD).

Intro / Verses

Playing the chords in open position will sound fine, but I recommend using the little moving chord shape that James Bay uses, which might even be easier! You just need (fretting hand) fingers 1 and 4 for the main riff. Because you're moving high up the fretboard, you'll need a guitar with a cutaway. The riff is played fingerstyle, using the thumb to play the bass notes and any finger for the top notes.

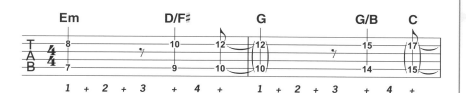

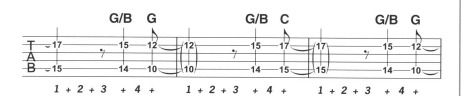

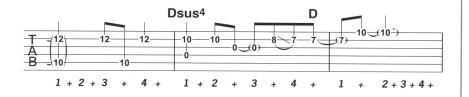

Hold Back The River

Words & Music by James Bay & Iain Archer

♩=135

Intro

| Em D/F♯ | G G/B | C G/B | G G/B |
| C G/B | G | Dsus⁴ | D |

Verse 1

|Em D/F♯|G   G/B |C   G/B G
Tried to   keep you close to   me,
G/B |C G/B |G |Dsus⁴ D |
But life got   in between.
|Em D/F♯|G   G/B |C G/B |G
Tried to   square not be - ing   there,
G/B |C G/B |G |Dsus⁴   D |
But say that I should've   been.

Chorus 1

C   C   C   C
Hold back the river, let me look in your eyes, hold back the river, so I
      G   G
Can stop for a minute and see where you hide,
G   G
Hold back the river, hold back.

Link 1

| Em D/F♯ | G |

Verse 2

Once upon a different life,
We rode our bikes into the sky.
But now we're caught against the tide,
Those distant days all flashing by.

Chorus 2

C   C   C   C
Hold back the river, let me look in your eyes, hold back the river, so I
      G   G
Can stop for a minute and be by your side,
G   D
Hold back the river, hold back.
Hold back the river, let me look in your eyes, hold back the river, so I
Can stop for a minute and see where you hide,
Hold back the river, hold back.

Link 2

Chords as Intro *(Vocals 'Oh')*

Bridge 1

G   G   G   G
Lonely wa - ter, lonely wa - ter,
             C   C   Am   Am   *(2°)* **N.C.**
Won't you let us wa - nder,   let us hold each other.   *(Repeat Bridge)*

Chorus 3

As Chorus 2

© COPYRIGHT 2014 KOBALT MUSIC SERVICES LIMITED/B UNIQUE MUSIC.
KOBALT MUSIC PUBLISHING LIMITED.
ALL RIGHTS RESERVED. INTERNATIONAL COPYRIGHT SECURED.

Stage 1　Stage 2　Stage 3　Stage 4　Stage 5　Stage 6　Stage 7　Stage 8　Stage 9　Bonus

Stage 1
Stage 2
Stage 3
Stage 4
Stage 5
Stage 6
Stage 7
Stage 8
Stage 9
Bonus

Bridge 2

G		G	G		G	

Lonely wa - ter, lonely wa - ter,

         C   C   Am *(1°)* C *(2°)* N.C.

Won't you let us wa - nder,   let us hold each other.   *(Repeat Bridge)*

Outro | Em D/F♯ | G G/B | C G/B | G G/B |

                      | C G/B | G | D |

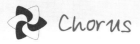

Chorus

When we get to the chorus you can use standard open chords but if you want to recreate the recording there are some funkier grips that James uses which aren't too tricky. For the C and D chords, James uses his thumb to play the bass note—this is challenging, so leave out the bass note if you're a beginner. These chords are unusual, and may require extra practice. Remember, you can always use regular open chords—it'll still sound great!

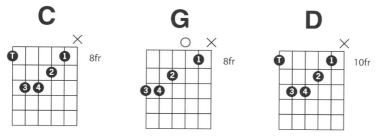

The strumming for the chorus is down-strums on every eighth-note, and to give it a bit more excitement you can place an accent on beats 2 and 4 (the backbeat).

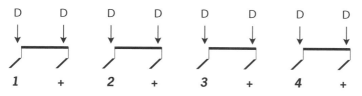

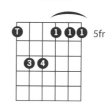

The bridge uses more or less the same chords but adds an Am, which you can of course play as an open chord, but James uses a lovely grip further up the neck—another addition to your chord vocabulary!

Me And Julio Down By The Schoolyard

Words & Music by Paul Simon

Stage 1
Stage 2
Stage 3
Stage 4
Stage 5
Stage 6
Stage 7
Stage 8
Stage 9
Bonus

♩=212

A

Intro ‖: A D | A E :‖ *Play x7*

Verse 1
  A   A
The mama pyjama rolled out of bed,
    A   D D
And she ran to the police station.
     E   E
When the papa found out, he be - gan to shout,
    E   A A (N.C.)
And he started the investi - gation.
      E E   A A
It's against the law, it was against the law,
      E E   A A
What the mama saw, it was against the law.

D(6)

Verse 2
  A   A
The mama looked down and spit on the ground
  A   D   D
Every time my name gets mentioned.
 E   E
Papa said, 'Oy, if I get that boy
     E   A |A
I'm gonna stick him in the house of de - tention.' (Well I'm on...)

E

Chorus 1
(N.C.) |D D   A   A
Well I'm on my way, I don't know where I'm goin'.
      D D |A   B7 |E
I'm on my way, I'm takin' my time but I don't know where.
        D |D G |A A
Goodbye to Rosie, the queen of Co - rona.
      |A G |D   E |A D|A E |
See you me and Julio down by the schoo - lyard.
      |A G |D   E |A D|A E |
See you me and Julio down by the schoolyard.

Instr. |D |A |D |A B7 E |

|D G A   ‖: A G D E | A D A E :‖ E N.C. |

Verse 3
Whoa, in a couple of days they're come and take me away,
But the press let the story leak.

(chords as verse 2)
And when the radical priest come to get me released
We was all on the cover of *Newsweek*.

Chorus 2
And I'm on my way, I don't know where I'm goin'.
I'm on my way, I'm takin' my time, but I don't know where.
Goodbye to Rosie, the queen of Corona.
See you me and Julio down by the schoolyard.
See you me and Julio down by the schoolyard.
See you me and Julio down by the schoolyard.

Coda ‖: A D A E :‖ *Repeat to fade*

© COPYRIGHT 1971 PAUL SIMON (BMI).
ALL RIGHTS RESERVED. INTERNATIONAL COPYRIGHT SECURED.

Introduction

This is a fantastic and challenging Paul Simon song. It uses simple chords but the real fun is with the rhythm (which is often the case).

Strumming

The strumming for this song is the real test, so start by playing just one strum per chord change (which will be once or twice a bar) and getting used to the structure of the song. You'll find that some of the chords change in expected places, which is part of the fun.

The most common strumming pattern is a quick, two-bar chord sequence which you'll hear during the intro. Really focus on this pattern before continuing with the lesson. Make sure you notice the 'pushed' A chord that comes on the '+' after beat 4. Lets call this Pattern 1.

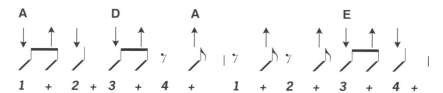

The challenge comes when chords change in odd places and we need a one-bar pattern too! Generally if there are two bars of a chord it will take Pattern 1, and if there is a third bar of a chord, that third bar will take this pattern, which we'll call Pattern 2.

For Verse 1 you'll play Pattern 1, then 2, then 1, then 1 again (noting that this time there is a chord change in the middle, and it's pushed) and then stop for the 'N.C'. You'll then play Pattern 1 four more times to reach the end of the verse. Verse 2 is the same as the first chunk (up to the stop) of Verse 1. The chorus will take Pattern 1 six times, but watch out for some pushed chords (the E after the B7 and the G before the A). For the key lines, where you sing 'Me and Julio…', it will take Pattern 2 twice (for the A G D E) and then Pattern 1 as we did for the intro.

Finally, I've included some of the more advanced chord grips too!

Wicked Game

Words & Music by Chris Isaak

♩=112

Chord sequence throughout:

Intro ‖: Bm | A | E | E :‖

Verse 1
The world was on fire,
No-one could save me but you,
Strange what desire will make foolish people do.
I never dreamed that I'd meet somebody like you
And I never dreamed that I'd lose somebody like you.

Chorus 1
No, I don't want to fall in love,
(This love is only gonna break your heart,)
No, I don't want to fall in love.
(This love is only gonna break your heart.)
With you, with you.

Verse 2
What a wicked game you play
To make me feel this way.
What a wicked thing to do
To let me dream of you.
What a wicked thing to say
You never felt this way.
What a wicked thing to do
To make me dream of you

Chorus 2
And I wanna fall in love,
(This love is only gonna break your heart,)
No, I wanna fall in love
(This love is only gonna break your heart.)
With you.

Guitar Solo *Play sequence x4*

Verse 3
The world was on fire,
No-one could save me but you,
Strange what desire will make foolish people do.
I never dreamed that I'd love somebody like you
And I never dreamed that I'd lose somebody like you.

Chorus 3
No, I wanna fall in love (this love is only gonna break your heart,)
No, I wanna fall in love (this love is only gonna break your heart,)
With you, (This love is only gonna break your heart,)
With you. (This love is only gonna break your heart.)

Repeat Chorus (vocals ad lib.)

Outro Nobody loves no-one.

Bm

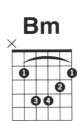

© COPYRIGHT 1989 C. ISAAK MUSIC PUBLISHING COMPANY.
WARNER/CHAPPELL MUSIC LIMITED.
ALL RIGHTS RESERVED. INTERNATIONAL COPYRIGHT SECURED.

Introduction

Chris Isaak's lovely song has a few challenges. The first is a B minor chord, which is a proper barre chord, although not a particularly hard one. There is no open chord version and I suspect the majority of you will be able to play it with a little practice.

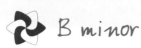 B minor

To play the Bm chord, start by playing an Am chord as if you didn't have a first finger, so make the same shape but using fingers 2, 3 and 4. Then slide that shape up two frets and lay your first finger down to cover all the frets on fret 2—see the diagram opposite. Now move finger 1 down so the tip is no longer pressing down on string 6, just touching (and therefore muting) it. Note that the barre only needs to press down on strings 5 and 1, so don't worry if the barre is a bit bent.

Strumming and riff

The strumming should be kept pretty simple for this song. 'Old Faithful' (see page 19) works well, but feel free to experiment with this or other patterns.

I recommend listening closely and learning some of the guitar lines by ear, which will be the best strategy. They're mostly around open position so have a go, and develop your aural skills.

The riff itself is quite specific, so I have included a TAB of it below:

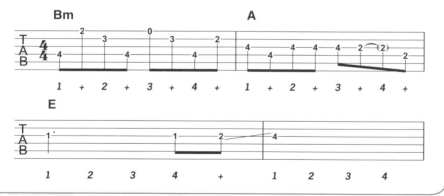

Stage 1
Stage 2
Stage 3
Stage 4
Stage 5
Stage 6
Stage 7
Stage 8
Stage 9
Bonus

243

Proud Mary

Words & Music by John Fogerty

♩=118

Intro

| C A | C A | C A G | F   D | D | | D | |

Verse 1

D   D
Left a good job in the city
D   D
Working for The Man every night and day,
D   D
And I never lost a minute of sleeping
D   D
Worrying 'bout the way things might have been.
A⁷   A⁷
Big wheel keep on turning,
Bm   Bm
Proud Mary keep on burning.

Chorus 1

D   D   D   D
Rolling, rolling, rolling on a river.

Verse 2

Cleaned a lot of plates in Memphis,
Pumped a lot of pain down in New Orleans,
But I never saw the good side of the city
Till I hitched a ride on a river-boat queen.
Big wheel keep on turning,
Proud Mary keep on burning.

Chorus 2

As Chorus 1

Link 1

| C A | C A | C A G | F   D | D | | D | |

Guitar solo

‖: D | D | D | D   :‖

| A | A | Bm | Bm |

Chorus 3

As Chorus 1

Link 2

| C A | C A | C A G | F   D | D | | D | |

Verse 3

If you come down to the river
Bet you gonna find some people who live.
You don't have to worry 'cause you have no money,
People on the river are happy to give.
Big wheel keep on turning,
Proud Mary keep on burning.

Chorus 4

‖: D   D   D   D
Rolling, rolling, rolling on a river. :‖ *(Play x4 then fade)*

© COPYRIGHT 1968 JONDORA MUSIC, USA.
BURLINGTON MUSIC COMPANY LIMITED.
ALL RIGHTS RESERVED. INTERNATIONAL COPYRIGHT SECURED.

Stage 1 · Stage 2 · Stage 3 · Stage 4 · Stage 5 · Stage 6 · Stage 7 · Stage 8 · Stage 9 · Bonus

Introduction

Our final Creedence Clearwater Revival track is one of the all-time greatest songs. It's not particularly tricky but it's got a bit of B minor action and a couple of rhythmic figures that you'll have to pay attention to!

 Intro

Let's start with the intro—follow the rhythm as shown below and you should be fine. Count along if you need to but your best bet is to practise it slowly and really make sure you get it right. Watch out for the D chord, which comes in a bit earlier than you might expect, at the very end of the intro 'riff'. If you're playing in a band, you'll get into all kinds of trouble if you miss that 'early' D chord out!

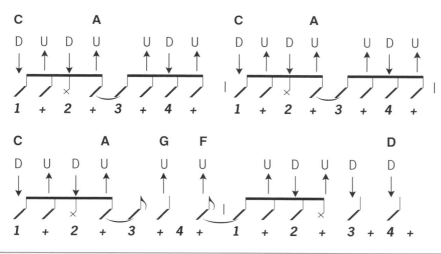

 B minor

In the verses, you'll encounter the Bm barre chord. It's often thought of as the easiest barre chord grip and although beyond beginner level, it's a good one to get started with.

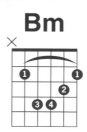

Bm

Stage 1
Stage 2
Stage 3
Stage 4
Stage 5
Stage 6
Stage 7
Stage 8
Stage 9
Bonus

Stage 1
Stage 2
Stage 3
Stage 4
Stage 5
Stage 6
Stage 7
Stage 8
Stage 9
Bonus

Ziggy Stardust

Words & Music by David Bowie

♩=78

Intro

‖: G5 D | Cadd9 G/B G5/A :‖ *(Play x4)*

Verse 1

G   Bm7   C
   Ziggy played guitar, jamming good with Weird and Gilly

              D
And the spiders from Mars.

                G   Em
He played it left hand but made it too far,

            A   C
Became the special man, then we were Ziggy's band.

Verse 2

Ziggy really sang, screwed up eyes and screwed down hairdo
Like some cat from Japan,
He could lick 'em by smiling, he could leave 'em to hang,
They came on so loaded man, well-hung and snow-white tan.

Chorus 1

|A5   G5 |F5   G5 |
   So where were the Spiders

|A5   G5 |F5   G5 |
   While the fly tried to break our balls?

|A5   G5 |F5 |
   Just the beer light to guide us,

  G5 |D   E
So we bitched about his fans and should we crush his sweet hands?

Link

‖: G5 D | Cadd9 G/B G5/A :‖

Verse 3

Ziggy played for time, jiving us that we were voodoo.
The kids were just crass,
He was the nazz with God-given ass.
He took it all too far but boy could he play guitar.

Chorus 2

Making love with his ego,
Ziggy sucked up into his mind.
Like a leper messiah
When the kids had killed the man I had to break up the band.

Coda

‖: G5   D | Cadd9 G/B G5/A :‖
                       (Oh

| G5   D | Cadd9 G/B G5/A | G   D |
 yeah!)   (Ooh - ooh.)

Cadd9   N.C.   G
     Ziggy played guitar.

© COPYRIGHT 1972 TINTORETTO MUSIC/MAINMAN-SAAG LTD NEW YORK.
CHRYSALIS MUSIC LIMITED, A BMG CHRYSALIS COMPANY/RZO MUSIC LIMITED/EMI MUSIC PUBLISHING LIMITED.
ALL RIGHTS RESERVED. INTERNATIONAL COPYRIGHT SECURED.

Stage 1
Stage 2
Stage 3
Stage 4
Stage 5
Stage 6
Stage 7
Stage 8
Stage 9
Bonus

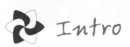 Introduction

This David Bowie classic is great fun to play and with a few embellishments, you can really bring the song to life. Although the original is played on a 'dirty' electric guitar it works great on acoustic too!

 Intro

Lets start with the intro—we begin with a G5 chord, familiar from AC/DC tunes, which will be easy to change to the D. On the D chord, pull your little finger on and off to create a little riff using the Dsus4 chord. Leaving finger 3 down we shift then to the Cadd9 which is a nice easy grip. The change to the G/B is easy too—just move finger 1 over to string 5, remove finger 2 and you're good. To get to the G5/A we just remove that first finger! Get the chords down first and then look at the rhythm.

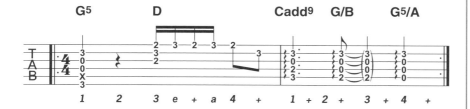

Strum the G chord on beat 1 and then mute with your strumming hand on beat 2. For the little riff on the D you'll strum D U D U D to a sixteenth- note count (see under the chords!). For the second bar of the riff just use down-strums, but observe the count carefully and as usual, listen to the original recording.

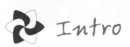 Chords

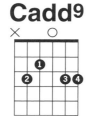

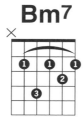

continued...

247

Ziggy Stardust (cont'd)

Verse strumming

During the verses we'll be looking at the acoustic strumming rather than the electric lead lines. There are many variations and accents to pick up on but I'd recommend the pattern below as a starting point. The obvious accents in Verse 1 are on the lyric 'spiders from Mars', where you'll play even eighth-note down-strums, on beats 3 + 4 + 1. Below is a 'summarised' version of the verse strumming.

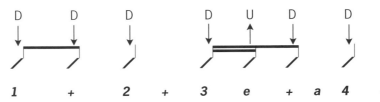

Power chords

When we hit the chorus you'll move to power chords. Follow the rhythm below—there is a cool embellishment whereby on the F you release finger 1 to play the open thickest string which creates a cool groove. Watch out for that last G power chord on the 'climb' back up too! See the TAB below for the chords and rhythm.

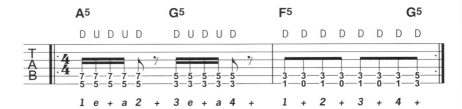

The end of the chorus gets a bit chaotic and there is no set pattern, so I would recommend playing even eighth-note down-strums (like the last part of the previous strumming pattern) but obviously the chords are different and you could add some up-strums to build the energy at the end of the chorus!

PRACTICE GUIDE

Stage 1

Stage 2

Stage 3

Stage 4

Stage 5

Stage 6

Stage 7

Stage 8

Stage 9

Bonus

Top 10 Practice Tips

1. Practise what you can't do, not what you can.

2. Practice makes permanent (not perfect). So get it right!

3. Start slowly and get it right before you speed up.

4. Using a timer saves time.

5. Focus on one element of a song at a time.

6. Try to practise a little every day, rather than a lot all on one day.

7. Keep track of your practice: use a practice schedule.

8. If it sounds good, it is good!

9. Playing and Practising are very different—don't confuse them.

10. The more you think, the more you stink! Practise until the part becomes instinctive.

Using Software

I would strongly suggest getting some software that will allow you to change the speed of a recording but not the pitch. I use one called *Transcribe!* but there are many others available, including *Audacity*, *Capo* and the *Amazing Slow Downer*.

Set the software to play the song at 50%, or at whatever speed you can practise in time with. Play along with the recording; use the 'cycle' feature to repeat one section (or the whole song) over and over. Once you are confident that you can play this section precisely, speed the track up, a little bit at a time. This may happen over the course of a few weeks, or in one practice session, depending on your ability and on the difficulty of the song.

Take time to learn how to use the software, in particular how to use the key commands (keyboard shortcuts). This will save you countless hours!

Justinguitar.com

**Justinguitar.com
Beginner's Course**
AM1001440R

**Justinguitar.com
Beginner's Songbook**
AM1005334

**Justinguitar.com
Beginner's Songbook
Volume II**
AM1011197

**Justinguitar.com
Intermediate Method**
AM1005202

- Refresh your beginner skills with the comprehensive *Justinguitar.com Beginner's Course* and the accompanying *Beginner's Songbook.* Then progress to the *Intermediate Method,* which will introduce further skills and techniques.

Collect the series…

**Justinguitar.com
Acoustic Songbook**
AM1005147R

**Justinguitar.com
Pop Songbook**
AM1005158

**Justinguitar.com
Blues Lead Guitar Solos**
AM1008183

**Justinguitar.com
Rock Songbook**
AM1005180

**Justinguitar.com
Vintage Songbook**
AM1005169

- Collect the other songbooks in the series. In each of the Acoustic, Pop, Rock and Vintage songbooks, you'll find 50 more songs specially chosen for guitarists who are looking to progress beyond beginner level. The *Blues Lead Guitar Solos* book presents 18 classic blues solos, the way they were played on the original recordings. All songbooks are also available as eBooks.